The Direct Primary Care Doctor's Daily Motivational Journal

THE DIRECT PRIMARY CARE DOCTOR'S DAILY MOTIVATIONAL JOURNAL

Douglas Farrago MD

Printed in the United States of America
First Printing, 2017
ISBN 9780692908952
www.authenticmedicine.com
ISBN: 0692908951

Praise for *The Direct Primary Care Doctor's Daily Motivational Journal*:

"A thought provoking book to work through on your own time to construct your ideal DPC practice. Whether you complete it in 3 months or 12 months, the answers to the questions are all your own. You are the only one who knows the specific passion and vision that you bring to Direct Primary Care! Questions range from broad, existential, personal questions to relationships to nuances of environment and service in your clinic. This appeals to new or seasoned DPC doctors or any physician who has a desire to improve their practice and the discipline of daily journaling will certainly improve many areas of life."

Kimberly Nalda MD, Direct Primary owner/physician at Rekindle Family Medicine, Wilmington, DE

Dr. Doug has provided the DPC community with another useful and informed "get it done" manual. Designed to walk you through the essentials of start up and building blocks to being an entrepreneur, *The Direct Primary Care Doctor's Daily Motivational Journal* allows you to break down the complexity of starting your own direct pay medical clinic. Dr. Doug is not only a writer but also a mentor, a successful DPC doc, a serial entrepreneur and long standing voice for authentic medicine.

Julie Gunther, MD owner/physician of SparkMD, Boise, Idaho

Starting a DPC clinic takes hard work. Douglas Farrago's newest book with a few minutes of reflection and writing by you can help you savor your successes and push on through the inevitable setbacks on this journey. I wish I'd had it my first year in, but am happy to have it now.

Michael Garrett MD, owner/physician at Direct MD, Austin, Tx

I think this is fantastic. I wish I had this available to me the year I converted my practice, although it is truly helpful now, too. DPC as we know, is not just a practice model, it is not just about all of us saying "we're not playing your game anymore" to insurance companies and the government; it is rebellious, disruptive, scary as hell, and after decades of being told what to do and how to do it, physicians opening DPC practices NEED to know that it is not all "eating rainbows and pooping butterflies." They need to know that it is okay to be scared, to not know what to do or how to handle it, that they HAVE to VALUE themselves and what they are doing by making this unbelievably scary leap. Thank you Doug, I think this is brilliant, simple, suggestive and will be much needed by many.

Kimberly Legg Corba DO, owner/physician at Green Hills Direct Primary Care, Allentown, PA.

This is the book that has been missing from DPC. The whys. Nuts and bolts of practice startup are one thing. Wrapping your mind around the esoteric nuances of this journey is equally important. This book is the perfect mentor to help physicians find their own voice and answer the questions they didn't even know they had.

Lisa Davidson DO, Owner/physician at Insight Primary Care, Denver, CO.

INTRODUCTION

Being a direct primary care doctor is pretty awesome. The connection to patients, the independence, the freedom, the extra time to spend with patients and even the income are definite pros to the job. That doesn't mean it is easy, though. In my last book, *The Official Guide to Starting Your Own Direct Primary Care Practice*, I tried to give you tips, ideas, technical advice and suggestions to start your own clinic. I also touched on some of the stressors and struggles that many of us go through. Others rarely talk about this last part and that is unfortunate because it is normal. We're human and no human journey is without its hurdles. That is why I try to make this a major focus of many of my lectures. One thing that helped me get through my tough times was keeping a journal. I used a cheap notebook where I wrote and wrote and wrote. I did it daily after I read a lot of self-help, business, and motivational books using their questions to prompt me. I eventually realized that these great questions are what helped me persist, stay determined and, I think, made me a better doc.

Why a question book?

One of my heroes is Tony Robbins, the motivational teacher who influenced me heavily in this area. I remember reading his stuff decades ago and listening to him when he said, "If you want better answers then you need to ask better questions?" Obviously he isn't the only one who believes this. Other present day great minds like Jay Abraham, Joe Polish, Tim Ferriss, Robin Sharma and Brian Tracy seem to think the same way as well. This is why I continue to collect questions from lectures, videos, podcasts or books. If it strikes a cord with me or helps me stay motivated then I keep it. This book is the result of this "hobby" and I have put the best questions I could find in one place for you. Many of these questions are not original or new other than making them applicable to direct primary care. Remember, though, these are just questions and prompts. You will find no real answers in here. You have to do all the work.

How to use this book

There is a year's worth of questions here. Use them. Each week starts with a preparation day on Sunday and ends with a reflection day on Saturday. Try to pick a time each day to think and write for 15 minutes. I recommend doing it in the morning as the book is set up that way. If you do it every day and try to get two months in without missing, you will create an awesome habit. Who knows what great ideas you'll come up with? You'll also have a notebook full of things to reflect upon at the end of the year.

If you want to save money then this book can be used year after year (if you leave it blank and write in another notebook) or you can just buy a new one each year. Why would you want to do it again? Well, we are different people at different stages of our careers. We see things differently and some of these questions will inspire again and again. In other words, this concept works for beginners to the very experienced docs. Trust me, it is really cool to look back and reflect upon past answers to see how much you have grown as a person and as a doctor.

A little advice

You will see themes in these questions. I really tried hard not to be redundant, but that's not easy for 365 days. Still, there is nothing wrong with phrasing questions differently or even repeating them in order to reinforce the message. In other words, "similar" questions will come up. There is a reason for that. I believe in order to be successful in this job you need to reflect on the good you are doing. You need to smile and have fun. You need to be grateful. And you need to connect to others. That is all I have to say on that. The rest is up to you.

Week One (Sunday): Planning your week is a great start to mastering the craft of being a DPC doctor. Here are some things to think about, but feel free to only answer one or even something else entirely:

- What things can you do this week to become the doctor you've always wanted to be?
- What things can you do this week to work on your physical and mental self (working out, meditation, nature walks, sleep, reading, etc.)?
- What things can you do this week to improve your business (marketing, advertising, fixing up the office, etc.)?
- Lastly, what three small wins do you want to accomplish this week?

Week One (Monday): Opening up a DPC practice may be the bravest thing you ever did in medicine or in life. It's now up to you to succeed or fail. List ten reasons why your practice will succeed and/or why it cannot fail.

_____
_____
_____
_____
_____
_____
_____
_____
_____
_____
_____
_____
_____
_____
_____
_____
_____
_____

Week One (Tuesday): What are you committed to getting done in your dream of being the doctor you always wanted to be? Is it learning something new (procedure, style of medicine, technology)? Or maybe it is in your attitude. For example, "I am committed to being compassionate, personable, caring....". Just brainstorm here and start writing.

_____
_____
_____
_____
_____
_____
_____
_____
_____
_____
_____
_____
_____
_____
_____
_____
_____

Week One (Wednesday): Are you overwhelmed in life? Where are some areas where you are feeling pressure? List them. What is causing it? What are some things you can to do to fix it?

_____
_____
_____
_____
_____
_____
_____
_____
_____
_____
_____
_____
_____
_____
_____
_____
_____
_____
_____

Week One (Thursday): Who could you be networking with to expand your DPC practice or to just expand your brain? Someone whose business you admire? An author of a book or article you might connect with online? A member of a local church group or hobby group? Someone from the local "leads" group? Just start thinking and write your ideas down here.

_____
_____
_____
_____
_____
_____
_____
_____
_____
_____
_____
_____
_____
_____
_____

Week One (Friday): Are there any ways you can give your patients a better experience at your practice? Think Disney. Think Starbucks. Music? Coffee? Providing a snack after getting blood taken? Anything. Close your eyes and start thinking of establishments you have been to where you had a great experience. What brought on that feeling? Can you copy that in your office?

_____

_____

_____

_____

_____

_____

_____

_____

_____

_____

_____

_____

_____

_____

_____

_____

_____

_____

Week One (Saturday): How did the week go? Pick out things that went well. Did you help people? What did you accomplish? What could you have done even better? How about those three small wins you wrote down on Sunday? Did you accomplish them? Or just review what you wrote each day and put some of your thoughts down here.

_____

_____

_____

_____

_____

_____

_____

_____

_____

_____

_____

_____

_____

_____

_____

_____

_____

_____

WEEK TWO

Week Two (Sunday): It's time to plan your week again. Here are some things to think about, but feel free to only answer one or even something else entirely:

- What things can you do this week to become the doctor you've always wanted to be?
- What things can you do this week to work on your physical and mental self (working out, meditate, nature walks, sleep, reading, etc.)?
- What things can you do this week to improve your business (marketing, advertising, fixing the office, etc.)?
- Lastly, what three small wins do you want to accomplish this week?

Week Two (Monday): List some of the activities in your job that give you your greatest sense of meaning and purpose in life. Is it helping people to change their behaviors? Is it getting people on the right medication? Maybe it is just connecting with people? List as much as you can here and try to go deep with it.

_____
_____
_____
_____
_____
_____
_____
_____
_____
_____
_____
_____
_____
_____
_____
_____
_____

Week Two (Tuesday): What needs to happen in the next 3, 6, 12 and 18 months to move you forward on your path to becoming a successful DPC doc? List some goals. For example, how many patients you want, how much money you need to make monthly, getting some press in the local papers, or changes in your physical office space, etc. List them out below.

_____
_____
_____
_____
_____
_____
_____
_____
_____
_____
_____
_____
_____
_____
_____
_____
_____

Week Two (Wednesday): What about your practice are you thankful for? For example: staff, your patients, etc. We need to appreciate even the small things in life like the fact you are finally in control or you have that piece of equipment you always wanted.

_____

_____

_____

_____

_____

_____

_____

_____

_____

_____

_____

_____

_____

_____

_____

_____

_____

_____

Week Two (Thursday): You need less than you think. You don't need the most expensive equipment, a large staff, new furniture, or a large office with the greatest location. You don't need a large marketing budget, a ton of money to live off of while you ramp up, or an administrator to hold your hand while you learn the business. You do need perseverance and determination. Make a list of why you have what it takes to succeed?

_____

_____

_____

_____

_____

_____

_____

_____

_____

_____

_____

_____

_____

_____

_____

_____

Week Two (Friday): What are you most proud of in life right now? How about the fact that you are independent of the hospital or the government? How about the patients you have helped? How about having a great family? List as much as you can here.

_____
_____
_____
_____
_____
_____
_____
_____
_____
_____
_____
_____
_____
_____
_____
_____
_____
_____

Week Two (Saturday): How did the week go? Pick out things that went well.   Did you help people? What did you accomplish? What could you have done even better? How about those three small wins you wrote down on Sunday? Did you accomplish them?   Or just review what you wrote each day and put some of your thoughts down here.

_____
_____
_____
_____
_____
_____
_____
_____
_____
_____
_____
_____
_____
_____
_____
_____
_____
_____

Week Three

Week Three (Sunday): It's time to plan your week again. Here are some things to think about, but feel free to only answer one or even something else entirely:

- What things can you do this week to become the doctor you've always wanted to be?
- What things can you do this week to work on your physical and mental self (working out, meditate, nature walks, sleep, reading, etc.)?
- What things can you do this week to improve your business (marketing, advertising, fixing the office, etc.)?
- Lastly, what three small wins do you want to accomplish this week?

Week Three (Monday): All jobs can be tough. Family medicine can be a struggle even for the best of us. Direct Primary Care is great but there will be struggles here as well. You are not alone. The key is getting perspective. Think of where you came from. List examples of how it used to suck in your prior job (residency, fee-for-service, hospital employed) and why it is better doing DPC? Write things down like "At least I don't have to _____ anymore".

_____
_____
_____
_____
_____
_____
_____
_____
_____
_____
_____
_____
_____
_____
_____
_____

Week Three (Tuesday): What things are out of your control that you need to let go of at this time? Admit it, we are all control freaks. That is part of being a doctor. The problem is you cannot control it all. List some things that your significant other or your staff or a family member or even a friend can do. List things that you just need to say no to and let go.

_____
_____
_____
_____
_____
_____
_____
_____
_____
_____
_____
_____
_____
_____
_____
_____
_____

Week Three (Wednesday): Up to this point, how have you made life better for you and your family? It is important to realize how far you have come. Your family knows it. The odds are you don't give yourself enough credit. Go back to when you were a kid and list how life has become better. Stay in the positive.

_____
_____
_____
_____
_____
_____
_____
_____
_____
_____
_____
_____
_____
_____
_____
_____
_____

Week Three (Thursday): What negative thoughts have been creeping into your mind lately? Today, you can let it out. Put down your doubts and fears. All of them. When you are done, go back and write down why each one is false.

_____
_____
_____
_____
_____
_____
_____
_____
_____
_____
_____
_____
_____
_____
_____

Week Three (Friday): How do you want to grow as a doctor in the next year? Not a simple question, I know. Do you want to be more knowledgeable? Do you want to be more caring? Do you want to be more at peace? Do you want to do more things in the field of DPC or family medicine?

_____

_____

_____

_____

_____

_____

_____

_____

_____

_____

_____

_____

_____

_____

_____

_____

_____

Week Three (Saturday): How did the week go? Pick out things that went well. Did you help people? What did you accomplish? What could you have done even better? How about those three small wins you wrote down on Sunday? Did you accomplish them? Or just review what you wrote each day and put some of your thoughts down here.

_____

_____

_____

_____

_____

_____

_____

_____

_____

_____

_____

_____

_____

_____

_____

_____

WEEK FOUR

Week Four (Sunday): It's time to plan your week again. Here are some things to think about, but feel free to only answer one or even something else entirely:

- What things can you do this week to become the doctor you've always wanted to be?
- What things can you do this week to work on your physical and mental self (working out, meditate, nature walks, sleep, reading, etc.)?
- What things can you do this week to improve your business (marketing, advertising, fixing the office, etc.)?
- Lastly, what three small wins do you want to accomplish this week?

Week Four (Monday): Ideas are great. Plans are super. But action is everything. What actions, in detail, can you take this week to move you closer to your goals in your DPC practice? For example, call two businesses or set up a local talk or become a vendor at local health fair. Rack your brain and then take some action. Actually do it.

_____
_____
_____
_____
_____
_____
_____
_____
_____
_____
_____
_____
_____
_____
_____

Week Four (Tuesday): How good is your pitch? Can you convince people in 30 seconds that they need you as their DPC doctor? Or how about why a business needs you? Or why a reporter needs to do a story on you? Write it down below (for each one) and practice it.

_____
_____
_____
_____
_____
_____
_____
_____
_____
_____
_____
_____
_____
_____
_____
_____

Week Four (Wednesday): Name your top three greatest strengths in life and how it will help you in your DPC practice. For example, you perseverance will never allow you to quit. List some more below.

_____
_____
_____
_____
_____
_____
_____
_____
_____
_____
_____
_____
_____
_____
_____
_____
_____

Week Four (Thursday): Don't forget about your health. Like in airplane, when those oxygen bags drop you are supposed to put in on yourself before your child because if you die then your child dies. Take care of yourself first. What can you do 10-15 min a day to work on yourself? Examples: pray, meditate, get out in nature, exercise, learn yoga, etc.

_____
_____
_____
_____
_____
_____
_____
_____
_____
_____
_____
_____
_____
_____
_____
_____

Week Four (Friday): What do you look forward to today and this weekend? It's okay to have fun. It's okay to dream. It's okay to NOT think about DPC for a little. What can you do to make yourself happier? A mini-vacation? Buy some new clothes? Write it down or your guilt will suppress it and you won't do it.

Week Four (Saturday): How did the week go? Pick out things that went well.   Did you help people? What did you accomplish? What could you have done even better? How about those three small wins you wrote down on Sunday? Did you accomplish them?   Or just review what you wrote each day and put some of your thoughts down here.

WEEK FIVE

Week Five (Sunday): It's time to plan your week again. Here are some things to think about, but feel free to only answer one or even something else entirely:

- What things can you do this week to become the doctor you've always wanted to be?
- What things can you do this week to work on your physical and mental self (working out, meditate, nature walks, sleep, reading, etc.)?
- What things can you do this week to improve your business (marketing, advertising, fixing the office, etc.)?
- Lastly, what three small wins do you want to accomplish this week?

_____
_____
_____
_____
_____
_____
_____
_____
_____
_____
_____
_____
_____
_____
_____
_____
_____
_____
_____
_____
_____
_____
_____
_____
_____
_____
_____
_____
_____
_____
_____
_____

Week Five (Monday): You cannot put whip cream on dog shit. Sorry if this offends anyone but I need to get my point across. First thing first, you need a great product. You can't move on to the next steps if your office is not delivering. Is your office giving a great product? List the ways your practice is of the highest quality.

_____

_____

_____

_____

_____

_____

_____

_____

_____

_____

_____

_____

_____

_____

_____

_____

_____

Week Five (Tuesday): What exciting things in particular about doing DPC do you have to look forward to? List some ideas. For example, brainstorming with other DPC docs, practicing medicine like you want to, being independent from the hospitals, etc. Or maybe it's going to a DPC conference and having social time with other DPC docs.

_____

_____

_____

_____

_____

_____

_____

_____

_____

_____

_____

_____

_____

_____

_____

_____

_____

_____

Week Five (Wednesday): To be successful in DPC you will need to do those things that other doctors never thought they had to do. This could be learning how to market your practice. This could be doing lots of "meet-and-greets". List some things that you can do to push this boulder uphill.

_____

_____

_____

_____

_____

_____

_____

_____

_____

_____

_____

_____

_____

_____

_____

_____

_____

_____

Week Five (Thursday): They say that your only limits are those limits you place on yourself. What limiting beliefs have held you back in the past? For example, some people feel they are too introverted to "sell" what they do. Others may think they don't know anything about business. List yours and then, more importantly, reflect upon why they are wrong.

_____

_____

_____

_____

_____

_____

_____

_____

_____

_____

_____

_____

_____

_____

_____

_____

Week Five (Friday): You are the best doctor in town. Why do I say this? For one, you spend more time with patients. For two, you truly care about people. Third…well, I could go on but now it is your turn to list them below.

_____
_____
_____
_____
_____
_____
_____
_____
_____
_____
_____
_____
_____
_____
_____
_____
_____

Week Five (Saturday): How did the week go? Pick out things that went well.   Did you help people? What did you accomplish? What could you have done even better? How about those three small wins you wrote down on Sunday? Did you accomplish them?   Or just review what you wrote each day and put some of your thoughts down here.

_____
_____
_____
_____
_____
_____
_____
_____
_____
_____
_____
_____
_____
_____
_____
_____

WEEK SIX

Week Six (Sunday): It's time to plan your week again. Here are some things to think about, but feel free to only answer one or even something else entirely:

- What things can you do this week to become the doctor you've always wanted to be?
- What things can you do this week to work on your physical and mental self (working out, meditate, nature walks, sleep, reading, etc.)?
- What things can you do this week to improve your business (marketing, advertising, fixing the office, etc.)?
- Lastly, what three small wins do you want to accomplish this week?

Week Six (Monday): What has to happen today or this week for you to feel good about yourself? As a person, spouse, parent or doctor? Do you need to get things done? Do you need to enjoy the day? Does the schedule need to run smoothly? Do you need time with your significant other? Write some things down.

_____
_____
_____
_____
_____
_____
_____
_____
_____
_____
_____
_____
_____
_____
_____
_____

Week Six (Tuesday): By starting your own DPC practice you will be ostracized, ridiculed, isolated or even hated. What do you need to remind yourself of in order to keep going? How can you emotionally buffer yourself from these haters? For example, "my first mandate is to help patients and jealousy by other doctors will never affect that", etc.

_____
_____
_____
_____
_____
_____
_____
_____
_____
_____
_____
_____
_____
_____
_____
_____
_____

Week Six (Wednesday): Your job is to help your patients get what they want. So the question is, what do most of them want? Make a list of common things they want from you. Do they want answers, someone to listen, to get better, to get healthier, a smile, etc.

_____

_____

_____

_____

_____

_____

_____

_____

_____

_____

_____

_____

_____

_____

_____

_____

_____

_____

_____

_____

Week Six (Thursday): What do you think your purpose in life is? Or what do you think your purpose is in opening up your DPC office? The answers may be the same, related or even contradictory. Think about this one for a bit.

_____

_____

_____

_____

_____

_____

_____

_____

_____

_____

_____

_____

_____

_____

_____

_____

_____

_____

_____

Week Six (Friday): There is nothing wrong with trying to be great in what you do. What do you do now that is great? In other words, visualize a patient saying "Dr. ( ) is great because he or she always......" or come up with something like "I feel great in my ability to...."

_____
_____
_____
_____
_____
_____
_____
_____
_____
_____
_____
_____
_____
_____
_____
_____
_____
_____

Week Six (Saturday): How did the week go? Pick out things that went well. Did you help people? What did you accomplish? What could you have done even better? How about those three small wins you wrote down on Sunday? Did you accomplish them? Or just review what you wrote each day and put some of your thoughts down here.

_____
_____
_____
_____
_____
_____
_____
_____
_____
_____
_____
_____
_____
_____
_____
_____
_____
_____

WEEK SEVEN

Week Seven (Sunday): It's time to plan your week again. Here are some things to think about, but feel free to only answer one or even something else entirely:

- What things can you do this week to become the doctor you've always wanted to be?
- What things can you do this week to work on your physical and mental self (working out, meditate, nature walks, sleep, reading, etc.)?
- What things can you do this week to improve your business (marketing, advertising, fixing the office, etc.)?
- Lastly, what three small wins do you want to accomplish this week?

Week Seven (Monday): If you were a patient (and, by the way, you should be) how would you want your doctor to act during your visit? Visualize that encounter. For example, I want a doctor that makes eye contact, who listens, who knows me, etc.

_____

_____

_____

_____

_____

_____

_____

_____

_____

_____

_____

_____

_____

_____

_____

_____

_____

_____

_____

Week Seven (Tuesday): It is time for some personal healing. We are all wounded in some way. It's called being human. It is particularly true being a doctor. What terrible experiences in the healthcare field did you have in the past? How can you let them go and forgive those involved? What have they taught you?

_____

_____

_____

_____

_____

_____

_____

_____

_____

_____

_____

_____

_____

_____

_____

_____

_____

_____

_____

_____

Week Seven (Wednesday): What matters most in your life right now? Even if your practice fails (the overwhelming odds says it won't) there are more important things to your life. What are they?

_____
_____
_____
_____
_____
_____
_____
_____
_____
_____
_____
_____
_____
_____
_____
_____
_____

Week Seven (Thursday): What habit, that if you did daily, would change your life the most? For example, eating right, spending time with your family, prayer, visualization, etc. Brainstorm some and pick one or two and start today!

_____
_____
_____
_____
_____
_____
_____
_____
_____
_____
_____
_____
_____
_____
_____
_____
_____

Week Seven (Friday): Do not underestimate the benefits of affirmations. Write down ten items of what your perfect DPC practice would look like in 3 to 5 years. Make it positive and detailed. For example, my practice will be filled with 600 patients. My patients will be happy with the incredible service I am giving them. And on and on.

_____
_____
_____
_____
_____
_____
_____
_____
_____
_____
_____
_____
_____
_____
_____
_____

Week Seven (Saturday): How did the week go? Pick out things that went well. Did you help people? What did you accomplish? What could you have done even better? How about those three small wins you wrote down on Sunday? Did you accomplish them? Or just review what you wrote each day and put some of your thoughts down here.

_____
_____
_____
_____
_____
_____
_____
_____
_____
_____
_____
_____
_____
_____
_____
_____
_____
_____

WEEK EIGHT

Week Eight (Sunday): It's time to plan your week again. Here are some things to think about, but feel free to only answer one or even something else entirely:

- What things can you do this week to become the doctor you've always wanted to be?
- What things can you do this week to work on your physical and mental self (working out, meditate, nature walks, sleep, reading, etc.)?
- What things can you do this week to improve your business (marketing, advertising, fixing the office, etc.)?
- Lastly, what three small wins do you want to accomplish this week?

Week Eight (Monday): My favorite quote from Steve Martin is "Be so good they can't ignore you." Are you being "so good" as a physician that people will be dying to join your practice? Where are areas you could be better?

_____

_____

_____

_____

_____

_____

_____

_____

_____

_____

_____

_____

_____

_____

_____

_____

_____

_____

Week Eight (Tuesday): They say it takes an irritated oyster to make a pearl. What are you irritated about? List the things that made you mad enough to make the leap into Direct Primary Care or that make you mad enough now to keep you in the DPC world.

_____

_____

_____

_____

_____

_____

_____

_____

_____

_____

_____

_____

_____

_____

_____

_____

_____

_____

_____

Week Eight (Wednesday): What is your philosophy as a doctor? This seems simple but it isn't. Think about it and just start writing to tease it out.

_____

_____

_____

_____

_____

_____

_____

_____

_____

_____

_____

_____

_____

_____

_____

_____

_____

_____

_____

Week Eight (Thursday): Teaching makes you a better doctor. When you teach patients versus telling patients, they do better. When you teach medical students or residents about DPC, then you feel better about what you do. Find ways to teach people. Brainstorm ways to contact a residency, a medical school, or even other health professionals. They may also be your biggest and best word of mouth after they spend time with you. So, how can you get the word out for others to do shadowing in your office?

_____

_____

_____

_____

_____

_____

_____

_____

_____

_____

_____

_____

_____

_____

_____

_____

Week Eight (Saturday): The perfect job does not exist. You must create it. I found that in an ad and taped it to my first workbook. You have now created your DPC job. Is it perfect? Probably not but you are moving in the right direct. What would your perfect DPC practice look like? Visualize and then write below.

_____

_____

_____

_____

_____

_____

_____

_____

_____

_____

_____

_____

_____

_____

_____

_____

_____

Week Eight (Sunday): How did the week go? Pick out things that went well. Did you help people? What did you accomplish? What could you have done even better? How about those three small wins you wrote down on Sunday? Did you accomplish them? Or just review what you wrote each day and put some of your thoughts down here.

_____

_____

_____

_____

_____

_____

_____

_____

_____

_____

_____

_____

_____

_____

_____

_____

_____

_____

Week Nine

Week Nine (Sunday): It's time to plan your week again. Here are some things to think about, but feel free to only answer one or even something else entirely:

- What things can you do this week to become the doctor you've always wanted to be?
- What things can you do this week to work on your physical and mental self (working out, meditate, nature walks, sleep, reading, etc.)?
- What things can you do this week to improve your business (marketing, advertising, fixing the office, etc.)?
- Lastly, what three small wins do you want to accomplish this week?

Week Nine (Monday): Is being liked more important than being right or is being the best doctor you can be your goal? List some of the risks of doing things to be liked by patients that are medically inappropriate. For example, prescribing antibiotics because a patient wants it. List why doing the right thing is so important in these situations.

_____
_____
_____
_____
_____
_____
_____
_____
_____
_____
_____
_____
_____
_____
_____
_____
_____

Week Nine (Tuesday): To succeed you need to shamefully self-promote. List some ways you can do that. It may be as simple as talking about your practice at a dinner party to contacting a local news show to be a guest. Brainstorm some ideas and how you can say it in a humble manner.

_____
_____
_____
_____
_____
_____
_____
_____
_____
_____
_____
_____
_____
_____
_____
_____
_____
_____
_____

Week Nine (Wednesday): How will your life be better when your DPC practice is filled and successful? Be specific. More control over your destiny? More financial security? It will hurt less when patients decide to leave? List some ideas.

_____
_____
_____
_____
_____
_____
_____
_____
_____
_____
_____
_____
_____
_____
_____
_____
_____

Week Nine (Thursday): What would your perfect office day look like? How would the day run? What would your mood be? How would your interactions go? Is this happening now? If not, how can you make it happen?

_____
_____
_____
_____
_____
_____
_____
_____
_____
_____
_____
_____
_____
_____
_____
_____
_____
_____
_____

Week Nine (Friday): How do you want to be talked about by your patients? In other words, what would you want them saying to friends at a dinner party or social gathering? Word of mouth is everything. Make a list below.

_____

_____

_____

_____

_____

_____

_____

_____

_____

_____

_____

_____

_____

_____

_____

_____

_____

_____

Week Nine (Saturday): How did the week go? Pick out things that went well. Did you help people? What did you accomplish? What could you have done even better? How about those three small wins you wrote down on Sunday? Did you accomplish them? Or just review what you wrote each day and put some of your thoughts down here.

_____

_____

_____

_____

_____

_____

_____

_____

_____

_____

_____

_____

_____

_____

_____

_____

_____

_____

WEEK TEN

Week Ten (Sunday): It's time to plan your week again. Here are some things to think about, but feel free to only answer one or even something else entirely:

- What things can you do this week to become the doctor you've always wanted to be?
- What things can you do this week to work on your physical and mental self (working out, meditate, nature walks, sleep, reading, etc.)?
- What things can you do this week to improve your business (marketing, advertising, fixing the office, etc.)?
- Lastly, what three small wins do you want to accomplish this week?

_____

_____

_____

_____

_____

_____

_____

_____

_____

_____

_____

_____

_____

_____

_____

_____

_____

_____

_____

_____

_____

_____

_____

_____

_____

_____

_____

_____

_____

_____

_____

Week Ten (Monday): What or who inspires you in life? It could be a friend. It could be an athlete or a historical figure. Put their names down and list why they inspire you, what their attributes are and how it may help you to stay inspired in your DPC practice.

_____
_____
_____
_____
_____
_____
_____
_____
_____
_____
_____
_____
_____
_____
_____
_____

Week Ten (Tuesday): List some reasons why having a successful DPC practice will give you some peace in life. For example, "by having a DPC practice I get to spend more time with my family" or "I get to be more complete with my patients".

_____
_____
_____
_____
_____
_____
_____
_____
_____
_____
_____
_____
_____
_____
_____
_____
_____
_____
_____

Week Ten (Wednesday): What successes have you had in seeing patients? List some success stories and the role you played in them. These are major wins to celebrate.

_____
_____
_____
_____
_____
_____
_____
_____
_____
_____
_____
_____
_____
_____
_____
_____
_____
_____

Week Ten (Thursday): What makes you happy about your DPC practice? Maybe it is types of patients or families who are members? Maybe it is the type of visits (preventative care, etc.)? Also, what could make you happier if it happened?

_____
_____
_____
_____
_____
_____
_____
_____
_____
_____
_____
_____
_____
_____
_____
_____
_____
_____

Week Ten (Friday): How are you changing the rules of primary care by doing Direct Primary Care and how will this take over the industry so patients will be clamoring to be part of it?

_____

_____

_____

_____

_____

_____

_____

_____

_____

_____

_____

_____

_____

_____

_____

_____

_____

_____

Week Ten (Saturday): How did the week go? Pick out things that went well.   Did you help people? What did you accomplish? What could you have done even better? How about those three small wins you wrote down on Sunday? Did you accomplish them?   Or just review what you wrote each day and put some of your thoughts down here.

_____

_____

_____

_____

_____

_____

_____

_____

_____

_____

_____

_____

_____

_____

_____

_____

WEEK ELEVEN

Week Eleven (Sunday): It's time to plan your week again. Here are some things to think about, but feel free to only answer one or even something else entirely:

- What things can you do this week to become the doctor you've always wanted to be?
- What things can you do this week to work on your physical and mental self (working out, meditate, nature walks, sleep, reading, etc.)?
- What things can you do this week to improve your business (marketing, advertising, fixing the office, etc.)?
- Lastly, what three small wins do you want to accomplish this week?

Week Eleven (Monday): They say that person's life equals the total sum of his or her experiences. Have you had any other experiences that have enriched your life? How? What other experiences can you do even while running a DPC office?

_____

_____

_____

_____

_____

_____

_____

_____

_____

_____

_____

_____

_____

_____

_____

_____

_____

_____

Week Eleven (Tuesday): You need time off to refresh, to learn or to just get away. Go into your office schedule and set some time off in the next month or so. Are those days booked? You have to prepare. Start setting up vacation days over the next year or so and then put them in now. Get your birthday off and Doctors' Day off (March 30th) and some other special days off like your child or spouse's birthday or anniversary. Schedule them now or you won't take them off at the last minute. At the very least, take a half a day off. Don't wait or you will forget and won't do it. You NEED time for yourself, and make sure you set up it at least a year in advance! There is nothing much for you to write today. This is an action prompt only!

_____

_____

_____

_____

_____

_____

_____

_____

_____

_____

_____

_____

_____

_____

Week Eleven (Wednesday): What is the one thing you could do today or this week that will have the most impact in your life over the next year? Brainstorm a few things and explain why. It could be learning a new procedure for your office. It could be learning a language. It doesn't matter. Just put stuff down and explain why.

_____
_____
_____
_____
_____
_____
_____
_____
_____
_____
_____
_____
_____
_____
_____
_____
_____

Week Eleven (Thursday): Who has helped you get to this point in your life? Think back as a kid or student in elementary, middle, or high school. Who do your appreciate for their inspiration and help? How did they help? What would you tell them now?

_____
_____
_____
_____
_____
_____
_____
_____
_____
_____
_____
_____
_____
_____
_____
_____
_____
_____

Week Eleven (Friday): Many of the things in your practice that matter most don't require money, just effort. Where could you be applying more effort right now to make your DPC clinic outstanding and successful?

_____
_____
_____
_____
_____
_____
_____
_____
_____
_____
_____
_____
_____
_____
_____
_____
_____
_____

Week Eleven (Saturday): How did the week go? Pick out things that went well. Did you help people? What did you accomplish? What could you have done even better? How about those three small wins you wrote down on Sunday? Did you accomplish them? Or just review what you wrote each day and put some of your thoughts down here.

_____
_____
_____
_____
_____
_____
_____
_____
_____
_____
_____
_____
_____
_____
_____
_____
_____

Week Twelve

Week Twelve (Sunday): It's time to plan your week again. Here are some things to think about, but feel free to only answer one or even something else entirely:

- What things can you do this week to become the doctor you've always wanted to be?
- What things can you do this week to work on your physical and mental self (working out, meditate, nature walks, sleep, reading, etc.)?
- What things can you do this week to improve your business (marketing, advertising, fixing the office, etc.)?
- Lastly, what three small wins do you want to accomplish this week?

Week Twelve (Monday): What is it about your practice that you are so committed to that no offer (from a hospital, etc.) or opportunity would make you quit? Write, "I am committed to…."and list some things.

_____

_____

_____

_____

_____

_____

_____

_____

_____

_____

_____

_____

_____

_____

_____

_____

_____

_____

_____

_____

Week Twelve (Tuesday): Have you celebrated anything about your office yet? A certain milestone like how many patients you have? Or is there anything else you can celebrate about the office? List some things for this week and for the next 12 months. Make plans to celebrate these accomplishments or you won't do it.

_____

_____

_____

_____

_____

_____

_____

_____

_____

_____

_____

_____

_____

_____

_____

_____

_____

_____

_____

Week Twelve (Wednesday): What parts of what you do in DPC makes you the most proud? And why? How about in your personal life? And why? List them below.

_____
_____
_____
_____
_____
_____
_____
_____
_____
_____
_____
_____
_____
_____
_____
_____
_____

Week Twelve (Thursday): What do you need to change about yourself in order to become more successful in your DPC practice? Listen, we all can be better. We all have deficiencies (eye contact, being a better listener, etc.). Some can't be fixed. Some can. Brainstorm and think about what you can do to make yourself even better.

_____
_____
_____
_____
_____
_____
_____
_____
_____
_____
_____
_____
_____
_____
_____
_____

Week Twelve (Friday): What went wrong in the office this week and how can you fix it? What will you do to prevent it from happening in the future?

_____
_____
_____
_____
_____
_____
_____
_____
_____
_____
_____
_____
_____
_____
_____
_____
_____
_____

Week Twelve (Saturday): How did the week go? Pick out things that went well. Did you help people? What did you accomplish? What could you have done even better? How about those three small wins you wrote down on Sunday? Did you accomplish them? Or just review what you wrote each day and put some of your thoughts down here.

_____
_____
_____
_____
_____
_____
_____
_____
_____
_____
_____
_____
_____
_____
_____
_____
_____

Week Thirteen

Week Thirteen (Sunday): It's time to plan your week again. Here are some things to think about, but feel free to only answer one or even something else entirely:

- What things can you do this week to become the doctor you've always wanted to be?
- What things can you do this week to work on your physical and mental self (working out, meditate, nature walks, sleep, reading, etc.)?
- What things can you do this week to improve your business (marketing, advertising, fixing the office, etc.)?
- Lastly, what three small wins do you want to accomplish this week?

Week Thirteen (Monday): Are you putting in the time to make this DPC thing work? You may be working long hours and think that is effective but is it? Is there any possibility that you may be doing busy work? Sometimes working harder isn't working smarter. Make a list of areas you need to focus on and that you need to put the majority of your time into.

_____

_____

_____

_____

_____

_____

_____

_____

_____

_____

_____

_____

_____

_____

_____

_____

_____

Week Thirteen (Tuesday): Be careful of useless distractions. You may catch yourself on Facebook, You Tube, Twitter, or even email when you could be doing other things at work. Like what? Well, that is up to you but how about education, learning business techniques, reading, etc. List some distractions you need to limit. Come up with an action plan to do that.

_____

_____

_____

_____

_____

_____

_____

_____

_____

_____

_____

_____

_____

_____

_____

_____

_____

_____

Week Thirteen (Wednesday): Here is another thought experiment. If they were asked, what would your friends and family say are your strengths? List them. How can you build off them? Describe how you feel about each one.

Week Thirteen (Thursday): What are some small things you can do to make your office experience better for patients? Think sight, sound, smell, etc. Pretend you're a friend and start from the parking lot and walk in and look at the office in detail as if you've never seen it before. Or ask a friend to do the same. Be brutally honest, and then come up with an action plan to make things better.

Week Thirteen (Friday): Failures fuel us to make us stronger and to grow. What failures in life taught you great lessons in your past? How can that apply to your DPC practice?

_____

_____

_____

_____

_____

_____

_____

_____

_____

_____

_____

_____

_____

_____

_____

_____

_____

Week Thirteen (Saturday): How did the week go? Pick out things that went well.   Did you help people? What did you accomplish? What could you have done even better? How about those three small wins you wrote down on Sunday? Did you accomplish them?   Or just review what you wrote each day and put some of your thoughts down here.

_____

_____

_____

_____

_____

_____

_____

_____

_____

_____

_____

_____

_____

_____

_____

_____

_____

_____

WEEK FOURTEEN

Week Fourteen (Sunday): It's time to plan your week again. Here are some things to think about, but feel free to only answer one or even something else entirely:

- What things can you do this week to become the doctor you've always wanted to be?
- What things can you do this week to work on your physical and mental self (working out, meditate, nature walks, sleep, reading, etc.)?
- What things can you do this week to improve your business (marketing, advertising, fixing the office, etc.)?
- Lastly, what three small wins do you want to accomplish this week?

Week Fourteen (Monday): We are being asked questions or to solve problems all day. What, where and when can you give yourself 15 min of total solitude and silence a day? Think about it and then plan some time to do it this week. How about right before work or at lunch or when you get home. What can you do during that time? Meditate, pray, snooze, yoga?

_____

Week Fourteen (Tuesday): Large successes come from daily, small victories. Each Sunday you are asked about some victories. Review some of them now. Which small victories have you had in your DPC practice? List them below. How can you create more of them?

_____

Week Fourteen (Wednesday): Let's explore what you're passionate about. Patients are sold on your passion when you meet them. What are you passionate about in family medicine? In DPC? In life? Write these down below. That is what you tell prospective patients.

_____

_____

_____

_____

_____

_____

_____

_____

_____

_____

_____

_____

_____

_____

_____

_____

_____

_____

_____

Week Fourteen (Thursday): Are you authentic to yourself or are you playing the role of a doctor? Are you being true to yourself and your personality? If not, in what ways are you not? If so, how? List them. For example, are you doing useless and verbose notes that are trying to meet false standards? Are you acting like someone else and not showing your true personality? Are you too afraid to laugh and tell an appropriate joke or quip?

_____

_____

_____

_____

_____

_____

_____

_____

_____

_____

_____

_____

_____

_____

_____

_____

_____

_____

Week Fourteen (Friday): What new marketing techniques can you try? Are there some books you can buy or podcasts you can listen to that may help? Spend some time today looking through business books or finding new podcasts just on marketing and start learning. Write down some options.

_____

_____

_____

_____

_____

_____

_____

_____

_____

_____

_____

_____

_____

_____

_____

_____

_____

_____

Week Fourteen (Saturday): How did the week go? Pick out things that went well. Did you help people? What did you accomplish? What could you have done even better? How about those three small wins you wrote down on Sunday? Did you accomplish them? Or just review what you wrote each day and put some of your thoughts down here.

_____

_____

_____

_____

_____

_____

_____

_____

_____

_____

_____

_____

_____

_____

_____

_____

_____

_____

Week Fifteen

Week Fifteen (Sunday): It's time to plan your week again. Here are some things to think about, but feel free to only answer one or even something else entirely:

- What things can you do this week to become the doctor you've always wanted to be?
- What things can you do this week to work on your physical and mental self (working out, meditate, nature walks, sleep, reading, etc.)?
- What things can you do this week to improve your business (marketing, advertising, fixing the office, etc.)?
- Lastly, what three small wins do you want to accomplish this week?

Week Fifteen (Monday): People like to feel part of something. By being part of your practice, they get an "identity". They are part of a community. How can you reinforce this? Doing talks, celebrating holidays, or sending out newsletters? This builds loyalty as they have an identity by being part of your DPC practice. Brainstorm some ideas that may work for you.

_____

_____

_____

_____

_____

_____

_____

_____

_____

_____

_____

_____

_____

_____

_____

_____

Week Fifteen (Tuesday): Do not forget your education? Not only in medicine but also in business? What courses can you take to push you out of your comfort zone? Are you reading medical articles daily? Should you be? Are you listening to lectures? List some things you could be doing.

_____

_____

_____

_____

_____

_____

_____

_____

_____

_____

_____

_____

_____

_____

_____

_____

_____

_____

Week Fifteen (Wednesday): What would your perfect DPC practice look like after it is totally full and mature (let's say 5 years from now)? Visualize, for example, a future where you are showing a journalist or a family member around. Go into details about your future practice as if you are actually pointing things out or explaining it to them.

_____
_____
_____
_____
_____
_____
_____
_____
_____
_____
_____
_____
_____
_____
_____
_____
_____

Week Fifteen (Thursday): What happened on the job recently that made you smile or you can smile about now? Was it a cute kid during a well-child exam? Was it a joke a patient told you? How can you create more episodes like that?

_____
_____
_____
_____
_____
_____
_____
_____
_____
_____
_____
_____
_____
_____
_____
_____
_____
_____
_____
_____

Week Fifteen (Friday): Let's get weird. In what crazy ways can you get your message out about your DPC practice? Try to brainstorm some ideas no matter how stupid they may seem. For example, little brain stress balls with your logo on them, sponsoring a race or even skywriting from a plane. Let your imagination go wild.

_____

_____

_____

_____

_____

_____

_____

_____

_____

_____

_____

_____

_____

_____

_____

_____

_____

_____

Week Fifteen (Saturday): How did the week go? Pick out things that went well. Did you help people? What did you accomplish? What could you have done even better? How about those three small wins you wrote down on Sunday? Did you accomplish them? Or just review what you wrote each day and put some of your thoughts down here.

_____

_____

_____

_____

_____

_____

_____

_____

_____

_____

_____

_____

_____

_____

_____

_____

_____

Week Sixteen

Week Sixteen (Sunday): It's time to plan your week again. Here are some things to think about, but feel free to only answer one or even something else entirely:

- What things can you do this week to become the doctor you've always wanted to be?
- What things can you do this week to work on your physical and mental self (working out, meditate, nature walks, sleep, reading, etc.)?
- What things can you do this week to improve your business (marketing, advertising, fixing the office, etc.)?
- Lastly, what three small wins do you want to accomplish this week?

Week Sixteen (Monday): Are you connected enough to others? Isolation can cause trouble for DPC docs. Who could you connect to? Family, friends, business people, other DPC docs? How can you do it?

Week Sixteen (Tuesday): Are you excited to see people who are prospective patients? Or even your regular patients? Or are you bored? Even worse, do you seem disinterested to your patients? People want an accurate diagnosis, but they also want you to be interested in them. Do some reflection and ask yourself if this is happening and then list some ways you can show you are interested in your patients.

Week Sixteen (Wednesday): Who can you call this week to give you advice in reaching your goals or who can at least motivate you? Not someone to complain to, but someone who will inspire you because he/she has faced similar obstacles.

_____
_____
_____
_____
_____
_____
_____
_____
_____
_____
_____
_____
_____
_____
_____
_____
_____
_____

Week Sixteen (Thursday): They say that if you have everything, you appreciate nothing. If you have nothing, you appreciate everything. What are the littlest things in life you truly appreciate? Not the big ones like family. How about a great sunset or cup of coffee? List some below.

_____
_____
_____
_____
_____
_____
_____
_____
_____
_____
_____
_____
_____
_____
_____
_____
_____
_____
_____

Week Sixteen (Friday): Business is a not an evil term. Without understanding business you can't make money and keep the doors open and treat patients. List other ways business is actually a good term.

_____
_____
_____
_____
_____
_____
_____
_____
_____
_____
_____
_____
_____
_____
_____
_____
_____
_____
_____

Week Sixteen (Saturday): How did the week go? Pick out things that went well. Did you help people? What did you accomplish? What could you have done even better? How about those three small wins you wrote down on Sunday? Did you accomplish them? Or just review what you wrote each day and put some of your thoughts down here.

_____
_____
_____
_____
_____
_____
_____
_____
_____
_____
_____
_____
_____
_____
_____
_____
_____
_____
_____

WEEK SEVENTEEN

Week Seventeen (Sunday): It's time to plan your week again. Here are some things to think about, but feel free to only answer one or even something else entirely:

- What things can you do this week to become the doctor you've always wanted to be?
- What things can you do this week to work on your physical and mental self (working out, meditate, nature walks, sleep, reading, etc.)?
- What things can you do this week to improve your business (marketing, advertising, fixing the office, etc.)?
- Lastly, what three small wins do you want to accomplish this week?

Week Seventeen (Monday): Let's say you were NEVER allowed to retire. Would you change your practice, your priorities or how you paced yourself in the day? Would you keep all the same patients? What would change if you could never retire?

_____

_____

_____

_____

_____

_____

_____

_____

_____

_____

_____

_____

_____

_____

_____

_____

_____

_____

Week Seventeen (Tuesday): What creative thing could you do in your practice that makes the place different or puts your stamp on it? Think of different things such as something physical (coffee or protein bars after a blood draw) or something you do as a doctor (a type of treatment). We have talked about this before, but have you acted on it? Exactly. Let's try again, shall we?

_____

_____

_____

_____

_____

_____

_____

_____

_____

_____

_____

_____

_____

_____

_____

_____

_____

Week Seventeen (Wednesday): Are you not only delivering on your promised services but are you over-delivering? Prove it. Write down exactly where you are over-delivering. Write down where you are not and how to fix those gaps.

_____
_____
_____
_____
_____
_____
_____
_____
_____
_____
_____
_____
_____
_____
_____
_____
_____
_____
_____

Week Seventeen (Thursday): How has starting your DPC practice proven that you are living the life you dreamed of? For example, "I am finally the doctor I've always wanted to be" or "I am finally in control over my own destiny".

_____
_____
_____
_____
_____
_____
_____
_____
_____
_____
_____
_____
_____
_____
_____
_____
_____
_____
_____

Week Seventeen (Friday): It has been said that wisdom is taking your own advice. What advice do you give every day to patients that YOU are not following? Subconsciously, you are sabotaging yourself by being hypocritical. What steps can you take to fix this?

_____

_____

_____

_____

_____

_____

_____

_____

_____

_____

_____

_____

_____

_____

_____

_____

Week Seventeen (Saturday): How did the week go? Pick out things that went well. Did you help people? What did you accomplish? What could you have done even better? How about those three small wins you wrote down on Sunday? Did you accomplish them? Or just review what you wrote each day and put some of your thoughts down here.

_____

_____

_____

_____

_____

_____

_____

_____

_____

_____

_____

_____

_____

_____

_____

_____

WEEK EIGHTEEN

Week Eighteen (Sunday): It's time to plan your week again. Here are some things to think about, but feel free to only answer one or even something else entirely:

- What things can you do this week to become the doctor you've always wanted to be?
- What things can you do this week to work on your physical and mental self (working out, meditate, nature walks, sleep, reading, etc.)?
- What things can you do this week to improve your business (marketing, advertising, fixing the office, etc.)?
- Lastly, what three small wins do you want to accomplish this week?

Week Eighteen (Monday): Have you talked to your friends recently? Name some friends you need to connect with (at least three) and then do it. You get bonus points if they are not in the medical field so you can gain some different perspectives on life.

_____
_____
_____
_____
_____
_____
_____
_____
_____
_____
_____
_____
_____
_____
_____
_____

Week Eighteen (Tuesday): What else would you do in life if you knew it would not fail or you would not be embarrassed? This is just to get your creative juices flowing. It doesn't mean you need to quit your day job, but it may unlock some other passions you may have hidden deep down inside yourself.

_____
_____
_____
_____
_____
_____
_____
_____
_____
_____
_____
_____
_____
_____
_____
_____
_____

Week Eighteen (Wednesday): What is one thing you can do today or this week that will have the most impact on your practice in one, three, six or twelve months? Think. There has to be something. Make a move. Take a chance. Go for it.

_____

_____

_____

_____

_____

_____

_____

_____

_____

_____

_____

_____

_____

_____

_____

_____

_____

_____

Week Eighteen (Thursday): We physicians tend to speak a lot. We do it all day. We also need to listen more. Use today to listen more to patients and staff. Make it a game plan if you have to. Delay before replying. At the end of the day list some lessons you learned from this.

_____

_____

_____

_____

_____

_____

_____

_____

_____

_____

_____

_____

_____

_____

_____

_____

_____

_____

Week Eighteen (Friday): Rationalizing, complaining, and making excuses in life doesn't really help anyone. Sure there are forces out there beyond your control. Get over them…go around them…or go through them. If you want to be successful that is the only way. Now, list those things that you feel hold you back in life or in your DPC practice. Put down in writing those things that you make excuses for or rationalize about. In what way can you work through them and still be successful?

_____

_____

_____

_____

_____

_____

_____

_____

_____

_____

_____

_____

_____

_____

Week Eighteen (Saturday): How did the week go? Pick out things that went well. Did you help people? What did you accomplish? What could you have done even better? How about those three small wins you wrote down on Sunday? Did you accomplish them? Or just review what you wrote each day and put some of your thoughts down here.

_____

_____

_____

_____

_____

_____

_____

_____

_____

_____

_____

_____

_____

_____

_____

_____

WEEK NINETEEN

Week Nineteen (Sunday): It's time to plan your week again. Here are some things to think about, but feel free to only answer one or even something else entirely:

- What things can you do this week to become the doctor you've always wanted to be?
- What things can you do this week to work on your physical and mental self (working out, meditate, nature walks, sleep, reading, etc.)?
- What things can you do this week to improve your business (marketing, advertising, fixing the office, etc.)?
- Lastly, what three small wins do you want to accomplish this week?

Week Nineteen (Monday): What can YOU do at the office today or this week to bring some more joy and happiness to the job? List some things.

_____
_____
_____
_____
_____
_____
_____
_____
_____
_____
_____
_____
_____
_____
_____
_____
_____
_____
_____

Week Nineteen (Tuesday): What are ways you can go about attracting those patients you truly want in your practice? Take a second and visualize the patients you want to in your panel. Some call it making the perfect patient avatar. Where would you find them? How could you market to them?

_____
_____
_____
_____
_____
_____
_____
_____
_____
_____
_____
_____
_____
_____
_____
_____
_____
_____
_____

Week Nineteen (Wednesday): Do you know what a swipe file is? Basically, if you have some free time take a look at the ads in some popular magazines and the Internet. Which ones grab your fancy? Start collecting the ones you like and tweak them to work for your DPC practice. Maybe you change some wording or some images but start the process. List some magazines or web site, social media pages or click bait sites that you need to visit today. Make new ads similar to them for Facebook, etc.

_____

_____

_____

_____

_____

_____

_____

_____

_____

_____

_____

_____

_____

_____

_____

_____

Week Nineteen (Thursday): Always be paying attention to details and "broken windows". What are some things you could be working on in the office or in yourself? Look around the office. Then walk through the office in the same steps the patient would take. Would you make any changes? List them.

_____

_____

_____

_____

_____

_____

_____

_____

_____

_____

_____

_____

_____

_____

_____

_____

_____

_____

_____

Week Nineteen (Friday): What part of being a doctor or a DPC doctor energizes you? You know those times when you finish a patient visit and it feels like you are injected with a bolus of epinephrine? Think about those times and figure out what the cause was. Also, it is not a bad time to note somewhere, even in this journal, how often they occur. It may be more common than you think

_____

_____

_____

_____

_____

_____

_____

_____

_____

_____

_____

_____

_____

_____

_____

_____

Week Nineteen (Saturday): How did the week go? Pick out things that went well. Did you help people? What did you accomplish? What could you have done even better? How about those three small wins you wrote down on Sunday? Did you accomplish them? Or just review what you wrote each day and put some of your thoughts down here.

_____

_____

_____

_____

_____

_____

_____

_____

_____

_____

_____

_____

_____

_____

_____

_____

_____

_____

WEEK TWENTY

Week Twenty (Sunday): It's time to plan your week again. Here are some things to think about, but feel free to only answer one or even something else entirely:

- What things can you do this week to become the doctor you've always wanted to be?
- What things can you do this week to work on your physical and mental self (working out, meditate, nature walks, sleep, reading, etc.)?
- What things can you do this week to improve your business (marketing, advertising, fixing the office, etc.)?
- Lastly, what three small wins do you want to accomplish this week?

Week Twenty (Monday): Have you found a mentor? Someone you can learn from? Another DPC doc? A business person? List some people you can connect with and take some actionable steps to do so.

_____
_____
_____
_____
_____
_____
_____
_____
_____
_____
_____
_____
_____
_____
_____
_____
_____
_____
_____

Week Twenty (Tuesday): Make a list of the things in life you do that make you happy. Make a list of all the things you do every day. Compare the list. Adjust accordingly (credit for this one goes to speaker Dan Clark).

_____
_____
_____
_____
_____
_____
_____
_____
_____
_____
_____
_____
_____
_____
_____
_____
_____
_____
_____

Week Twenty (Wednesday): What have you learned from a book recently that relates to your success in DPC? Go to the most recent one and start writing some notes, tips and ideas below. Haven't read any books? What books could you be reading?

_____
_____
_____
_____
_____
_____
_____
_____
_____
_____
_____
_____
_____
_____
_____
_____
_____
_____

Week Twenty (Thursday): This one is a little rough and can seem negative, but don't let it be. What would your friends and family say are your weaknesses? List them. How can you improve on them?

_____
_____
_____
_____
_____
_____
_____
_____
_____
_____
_____
_____
_____
_____
_____
_____
_____
_____
_____
_____
_____
_____

Week Twenty (Friday): Do you have any specific interest inside the DPC model (i.e. dermatology, OMT, sports medicine)? Are there some new areas you can dive into? Brainstorm and list them here.

_____
_____
_____
_____
_____
_____
_____
_____
_____
_____
_____
_____
_____
_____
_____
_____
_____

Week Twenty (Saturday): How did the week go? Pick out things that went well. Did you help people? What did you accomplish? What could you have done even better? How about those three small wins you wrote down on Sunday? Did you accomplish them? Or just review what you wrote each day and put some of your thoughts down here.

_____
_____
_____
_____
_____
_____
_____
_____
_____
_____
_____
_____
_____
_____
_____
_____
_____

WEEK TWENTY-ONE

Week Twenty-One (Sunday): It's time to plan your week again. Here are some things to think about, but feel free to only answer one or even something else entirely:

- What things can you do this week to become the doctor you've always wanted to be?
- What things can you do this week to work on your physical and mental self (working out, meditate, nature walks, sleep, reading, etc.)?
- What things can you do this week to improve your business (marketing, advertising, fixing the office, etc.)?
- Lastly, what three small wins do you want to accomplish this week?

Week Twenty-One (Monday): You will not succeed or be happy in DPC unless you remind yourself why you are so passionate about it? Why is this job important for you? Even better, why is it so important for your patients? How are other patients losing out by not being in your practice?

_____

_____

_____

_____

_____

_____

_____

_____

_____

_____

_____

_____

_____

_____

_____

_____

_____

_____

Week Twenty-One (Tuesday): Be clear about who you are. What's most important to you in life? List below.

_____

_____

_____

_____

_____

_____

_____

_____

_____

_____

_____

_____

_____

_____

_____

_____

_____

_____

_____

_____

Week Twenty-One (Wednesday): Bartering is still good business. Could you trade some of your care for advertising, videotaping, print material, etc. Brainstorm some local places you can approach. Don't judge your ideas but just keep writing. (Be aware of tax implications here.)

_____
_____
_____
_____
_____
_____
_____
_____
_____
_____
_____
_____
_____
_____
_____
_____
_____
_____
_____

Week Twenty-One (Thursday): List some of your past detractors, negative colleagues and critics and what they said about you when you decided to take this jump into DPC. Now write how your forgive them. Take that weight off your back. They are the ones who are jealous of your DPC move and are hurting… not you (see Death Row Syndrome in my book).

_____
_____
_____
_____
_____
_____
_____
_____
_____
_____
_____
_____
_____
_____
_____
_____
_____
_____
_____
_____

Week Twenty-One (Friday): The Pareto Principle states that 80% of your success comes from 20% of your efforts? Where does that apply to your practice for marketing? Is it in Facebook? Dive deeper. Which 20% of those ads? Keep going using your other marketing strategies.

_____

_____

_____

_____

_____

_____

_____

_____

_____

_____

_____

_____

_____

_____

_____

_____

_____

Week Twenty-One (Saturday): How did the week go? Pick out things that went well. Did you help people? What did you accomplish? What could you have done even better? How about those three small wins you wrote down on Sunday? Did you accomplish them? Or just review what you wrote each day and put some of your thoughts down here.

_____

_____

_____

_____

_____

_____

_____

_____

_____

_____

_____

_____

_____

_____

_____

_____

_____

WEEK TWENTY-TWO

Week Twenty-Two (Sunday): It's time to plan your week again. Here are some things to think about. Here are some things to think about, but feel free to only answer one or even something else entirely:

- What things can you do this week to become the doctor you've always wanted to be?
- What things can you do this week to work on your physical and mental self (working out, meditate, nature walks, sleep, reading, etc.)?
- What things can you do this week to improve your business (marketing, advertising, fixing the office, etc.)?
- Lastly, what three small wins do you want to accomplish this week?

Week Twenty-Two (Monday): Being a doctor is a craft not a job. It is not an assembly line and, contrary to what administrators say, not everyone can do it. Not even close. If you ever get to watch the show Chef's Table on Netflix you will see how master chefs are celebrated. Why aren't great family docs? In what ways have you tried to master your craft? In what ways could you? The devil may be in the details. This could be following up with patients or really getting to know them and what they do. It could be going the extra mile on cases. You decide, but first write down some ideas.

_____

_____

_____

_____

_____

_____

_____

_____

_____

_____

_____

_____

Week Twenty-Two (Tuesday): What things can you possibly automate or delegate in order to streamline your practice and optimize it? List them. This extra time allows you to work on mastering your craft as noted yesterday.

_____

_____

_____

_____

_____

_____

_____

_____

_____

_____

_____

_____

_____

_____

_____

_____

_____

Week Twenty-Two (Wednesday): Do you surround yourself with the right people? This could be in the office, at home, or even online. Are they positive and energetic and aligned with your values or do they bring you down and suck the energy out of your life? List the energy givers and energy drainers in your life. Spend time with the former and less with the latter.

_____

_____

_____

_____

_____

_____

_____

_____

_____

_____

_____

_____

_____

_____

Week Twenty-Two (Thursday): It's time you dream a little and think big. Think of some crazy ways to improve, expand, or grow in the future. Would you have more partners? Would your office have a yoga studio, a gym, or maybe higher tech equipment? No judgment. Let your brain free flow and just keep writing.

_____

_____

_____

_____

_____

_____

_____

_____

_____

_____

_____

_____

_____

_____

_____

_____

_____

Week Twenty-Two (Friday): DPC is great but there is turnover. People are always thinking "what have you done for me lately". Your present customers are more important than trying to accrue new ones. What are you doing to keep impressing and connecting with your present customers? What else could you do? It may not be quantity but quality.

_____
_____
_____
_____
_____
_____
_____
_____
_____
_____
_____
_____
_____
_____
_____

Week Twenty-Two (Saturday): How did the week go? Pick out things that went well. Did you help people? What did you accomplish? What could you have done even better? How about those three small wins you wrote down on Sunday? Did you accomplish them? Or just review what you wrote each day and put some of your thoughts down here.

_____
_____
_____
_____
_____
_____
_____
_____
_____
_____
_____
_____
_____
_____
_____
_____
_____
_____

WEEK TWENTY-THREE

Week Twenty-Three (Sunday): It's time to plan your week again. Here are some things to think about, but feel free to only answer one or even something else entirely:

- What things can you do this week to become the doctor you've always wanted to be?
- What things can you do this week to work on your physical and mental self (working out, meditate, nature walks, sleep, reading, etc.)?
- What things can you do this week to improve your business (marketing, advertising, fixing the office, etc.)?
- Lastly, what three small wins do you want to accomplish this week?

Week Twenty-Three (Monday): What is it about your office (physical structure or service) that makes you proud? Go through the small things like the location to the big things like your staff and your care. Then describe why you are proud of them.

_____

_____

_____

_____

_____

_____

_____

_____

_____

_____

_____

_____

_____

_____

_____

_____

_____

Week Twenty-Three (Tuesday): What is the legacy you are leaving for future doctors? For medical students of the future, what would you like to be known for? Let go of your ego and brag a little here. You are changing the face of family medicine.

_____

_____

_____

_____

_____

_____

_____

_____

_____

_____

_____

_____

_____

_____

_____

_____

_____

_____

Week Twenty-Three (Wednesday): If someone woke you up in the middle of the night and asked what you do, what would you say? Quickly. Ok, not so quickly, but write it below and then trim it and make it more concise.   This is your mantra.

_____

_____

_____

_____

_____

_____

_____

_____

_____

_____

_____

_____

_____

_____

_____

_____

Week Twenty-Three (Thursday): Compared to what you were a year ago or even 5 years ago, how have your improved as a person?

_____

_____

_____

_____

_____

_____

_____

_____

_____

_____

_____

_____

_____

_____

_____

_____

_____

_____

Week Twenty-Three (Friday): Let's get simple.   Why do you practice medicine? Lists the reasons.

_____
_____
_____
_____
_____
_____
_____
_____
_____
_____
_____
_____
_____
_____
_____
_____
_____
_____

Week Twenty-Three (Saturday): How did the week go? Pick out things that went well.   Did you help people? What did you accomplish? What could you have done even better? How about those three small wins you wrote down on Sunday? Did you accomplish them?   Or just review what you wrote each day and put some of your thoughts down here.

_____
_____
_____
_____
_____
_____
_____
_____
_____
_____
_____
_____
_____
_____
_____
_____
_____

WEEK TWENTY-FOUR

Week Twenty-Four (Sunday): It's time to plan your week again. Here are some things to think about, but feel free to only answer one or even something else entirely:

- What things can you do this week to become the doctor you've always wanted to be?
- What things can you do this week to work on your physical and mental self (working out, meditate, nature walks, sleep, reading, etc.)?
- What things can you do this week to improve your business (marketing, advertising, fixing the office, etc.)?
- Lastly, what three small wins do you want to accomplish this week?

Week Twenty-Four (Monday): Why would patients brag about you and your office?   What kind of things do you envision or hope they are saying?

_____

_____

_____

_____

_____

_____

_____

_____

_____

_____

_____

_____

_____

_____

_____

_____

_____

Week Twenty-Four (Tuesday): Okay, homework time again. What are you doing to constantly learn: business, marketing, public speaking, or learning the newest trends in medicine?

_____

_____

_____

_____

_____

_____

_____

_____

_____

_____

_____

_____

_____

_____

_____

_____

_____

_____

_____

Week Twenty-Four (Wednesday): What are three bad habits you personally need to break? List them out and explain why it is so important to break them and how can you break them.

_____
_____
_____
_____
_____
_____
_____
_____
_____
_____
_____
_____
_____
_____
_____
_____
_____
_____
_____

Week Twenty-Four (Thursday): What has to happen for you to be prosperous and financially secure in life? Can you do this with your DPC practice? If not, should you be learning about investing your money? Brainstorm some ideas.

_____
_____
_____
_____
_____
_____
_____
_____
_____
_____
_____
_____
_____
_____
_____
_____
_____
_____
_____

Week Twenty-Four (Friday): What can you get rid of or simplify in your practice right now in order to make life easier? It could be staff. It could be troublesome patients. It could be the way you run the practice. List some ideas.

_____

_____

_____

_____

_____

_____

_____

_____

_____

_____

_____

_____

_____

_____

_____

_____

_____

_____

Week Twenty-Four (Saturday): How did the week go? Pick out things that went well. Did you help people? What did you accomplish? What could you have done even better? How about those three small wins you wrote down on Sunday? Did you accomplish them? Or just review what you wrote each day and put some of your thoughts down here.

_____

_____

_____

_____

_____

_____

_____

_____

_____

_____

_____

_____

_____

_____

_____

_____

_____

_____

_____

WEEK TWENTY-FIVE

Week Twenty-Five (Sunday): It's time to plan your week again. Here are some things to think about, but feel free to only answer one or even something else entirely:

- What things can you do this week to become the doctor you've always wanted to be?
- What things can you do this week to work on your physical and mental self (working out, meditate, nature walks, sleep, reading, etc.)?
- What things can you do this week to improve your business (marketing, advertising, fixing the office, etc.)?
- Lastly, what three small wins do you want to accomplish this week?

Week Twenty-Five (Monday): What have you done creatively recently? If very little, brainstorm some things you could do? Life can't be all about practicing medicine. Can you do something else? Art? Write? Build something? Think of some ideas.

_____

_____

_____

_____

_____

_____

_____

_____

_____

_____

_____

_____

_____

_____

_____

_____

_____

Week Twenty-Five (Tuesday): Find your office hook? What are you going to be known for? Value? Excellence? Accessibility? Exclusivity? Think about each one of these things and how they can apply to you. And then start thinking about a plan to hone in on one.

_____

_____

_____

_____

_____

_____

_____

_____

_____

_____

_____

_____

_____

_____

_____

_____

_____

_____

Week Twenty-Five (Wednesday): There are certain patients (we all have them) who can be over-utilizers. It is usually a small percentage, but they can kill you. That isn't why we did DPC. Also, too many of these will take spots from those patients who actually need them. My recommendation is to make a "no fly" list. These are names that my staff cannot put on the schedule ever unless the patient first emails me or if I approve it. Now, think of names to put on your list (use initials only) and share later with your staff.

Week Twenty-Five (Thursday): If you knew this was the last year of your life, what would you do differently? Are there any other dreams or projects you would start? Or would you just connect more with your friends and family?

Week Twenty-Five (Friday): Patients will quit. They will blame you or you will blame yourself. Please don't. Life is too short. Over 99% of the time they quit because of their issues, but they need to make you the scapegoat. List a few ways you won't take it personally. This could be repeating positive affirmations, talking through it with your staff or commiserating with another DPC doc or group.

_____
_____
_____
_____
_____
_____
_____
_____
_____
_____
_____
_____
_____
_____
_____
_____

Week Twenty-Five (Saturday): How did the week go? Pick out things that went well. Did you help people? What did you accomplish? What could you have done even better? How about those three small wins you wrote down on Sunday? Did you accomplish them? Or just review what you wrote each day and put some of your thoughts down here.

_____
_____
_____
_____
_____
_____
_____
_____
_____
_____
_____
_____
_____
_____
_____
_____
_____
_____

WEEK TWENTY-SIX

Week Twenty-Six (Sunday): It's time to plan your week again. Here are some things to think about, but feel free to only answer one or even something else entirely:

- What things can you do this week to become the doctor you've always wanted to be?
- What things can you do this week to work on your physical and mental self (working out, meditate, nature walks, sleep, reading, etc.)?
- What things can you do this week to improve your business (marketing, advertising, fixing the office, etc.)?
- Lastly, what three small wins do you want to accomplish this week?

Week Twenty-Six (Monday): What are you looking forward to most in life right now? This could be professionally, financially, or even family events or milestones. Start listing some things and tell why they are important to you.

_____

_____

_____

_____

_____

_____

_____

_____

_____

_____

_____

_____

_____

_____

_____

_____

_____

_____

Week Twenty-Six (Tuesday): Old habits are hard to break. We have talked about this before, but what time wasters can you get rid of to be more productive? Don't have any? Bullshit. Facebook, TV, and your Smartphone are a few. What about tasks that you could easily delegate? Think about some that relate to you.

_____

_____

_____

_____

_____

_____

_____

_____

_____

_____

_____

_____

_____

_____

_____

_____

_____

_____

Week Twenty-Six (Wednesday): What action can you take this week that would help you push uphill that boulder of building a successful practice?   Maybe doing more posts on social media? How about talking to an HR person at a company or speaking to an owner at a small business. Like Winnie the Pooh said, "think, think, think."

_____
_____
_____
_____
_____
_____
_____
_____
_____
_____
_____
_____
_____
_____

Week Twenty-Six (Thursday): Time to get negative again. What's isn't going so well in your life or in your office and how can you change things? But before you write that down, ask yourself why you need to change these things. Get specific on a plan.

_____
_____
_____
_____
_____
_____
_____
_____
_____
_____
_____
_____
_____
_____
_____
_____

Week Twenty-Six (Friday): What are some areas in life where you need more self-restraint or willpower? Is it on the job with certain patients or at home with your diet?   Think of some and list them here. Then think of some beliefs you have that must change in order to gain more self-restraint or will power.

_____
_____
_____
_____
_____
_____
_____
_____
_____
_____
_____
_____
_____
_____
_____
_____
_____
_____
_____
_____

Week Twenty-Six (Saturday): How did the week go? Pick out things that went well.   Did you help people? What did you accomplish? What could you have done even better? How about those three small wins you wrote down on Sunday? Did you accomplish them?   Or just review what you wrote each day and put some of your thoughts down here.

_____
_____
_____
_____
_____
_____
_____
_____
_____
_____
_____
_____
_____
_____
_____
_____
_____
_____
_____

Week Twenty-Seven

Week Twenty-Seven (Sunday): It's time to plan your week again. Here are some things to think about, but feel free to only answer one or even something else entirely:

- What things can you do this week to become the doctor you've always wanted to be?
- What things can you do this week to work on your physical and mental self (working out, meditate, nature walks, sleep, reading, etc.)?
- What things can you do this week to improve your business (marketing, advertising, fixing the office, etc.)?
- Lastly, what three small wins do you want to accomplish this week?

Week Twenty-Seven (Monday): Are you patient enough in your vision of your DPC practice? Remember, this is going to take one to two years to get good. Write down why you need to be more patient and then give examples of short term goals for the next 3, 6, 12, 18 and 24 months.

_____
_____
_____
_____
_____
_____
_____
_____
_____
_____
_____
_____
_____
_____
_____
_____
_____

Week Twenty-Seven (Tuesday): What are the biggest personal obstacles in life you need to overcome to reach the next level?

_____
_____
_____
_____
_____
_____
_____
_____
_____
_____
_____
_____
_____
_____
_____
_____
_____
_____
_____

Week Twenty-Seven (Wednesday): What things do you do differently from others that has made you successful in life and in your DPC practice?

_____
_____
_____
_____
_____
_____
_____
_____
_____
_____
_____
_____
_____
_____
_____
_____
_____
_____
_____
_____
_____

Week Twenty-Seven (Thursday): What about your practice are you most proud? Whether you started this journal at the beginning of your personal journey or maybe you are three years into your journey, there has to be something about your practice that you are proud of. Be vain. Just start listing things.

_____
_____
_____
_____
_____
_____
_____
_____
_____
_____
_____
_____
_____
_____
_____
_____
_____
_____
_____
_____

Week Twenty-Seven (Friday): What is the driving force behind your life? In starting your own DPC practice?

Week Twenty-Seven (Saturday): How did the week go? Pick out things that went well. Did you help people? What did you accomplish? What could you have done even better? How about those three small wins you wrote down on Sunday? Did you accomplish them? Or just review what you wrote each day and put some of your thoughts down here.

WEEK TWENTY-EIGHT

Week Twenty-Eight (Sunday): It's time to plan your week again. Here are some things to think about, but feel free to only answer one or even something else entirely:

- What things can you do this week to become the doctor you've always wanted to be?
- What things can you do this week to work on your physical and mental self (working out, meditate, nature walks, sleep, reading, etc.)?
- What things can you do this week to improve your business (marketing, advertising, fixing the office, etc.)?
- Lastly, what three small wins do you want to accomplish this week?

Week Twenty-Eight (Monday): What needs to happen today or this week to make you feel successful or happy? Is it helping people? Is it getting more press for your practice? List some things.

_____

_____

_____

_____

_____

_____

_____

_____

_____

_____

_____

_____

_____

_____

_____

_____

_____

_____

_____

_____

_____

Week Twenty-Eight (Tuesday): What is the most important action or thing you do or could to in order to most impact your patients' lives?

_____

_____

_____

_____

_____

_____

_____

_____

_____

_____

_____

_____

_____

_____

_____

_____

_____

_____

_____

_____

Week Twenty-Eight (Wednesday): What risks have you taken recently to advance your career or DPC practice? Have you done anything to come out of your comfort zone? What can you do to keep moving forward? Brainstorm some ideas.

_____
_____
_____
_____
_____
_____
_____
_____
_____
_____
_____
_____
_____
_____
_____
_____
_____
_____
_____

Week Twenty-Eight (Thursday): Your DPC practice cannot and should not appeal to everyone. Which groups or types of patients are not a good fit for your practice? Which are not?

_____
_____
_____
_____
_____
_____
_____
_____
_____
_____
_____
_____
_____
_____
_____
_____
_____
_____
_____

Week Twenty-Eight (Friday): What are you thankful for in life and who are you grateful for?

Week Twenty-Eight (Saturday): How did the week go? Pick out things that went well. Did you help people? What did you accomplish? What could you have done even better? How about those three small wins you wrote down on Sunday? Did you accomplish them? Or just review what you wrote each day and put some of your thoughts down here.

Week Twenty-Nine

Week Twenty-Nine (Sunday): It's time to plan your week again. Here are some things to think about, but feel free to only answer one or even something else entirely:

- What things can you do this week to become the doctor you've always wanted to be?
- What things can you do this week to work on your physical and mental self (working out, meditate, nature walks, sleep, reading, etc.)?
- What things can you do this week to improve your business (marketing, advertising, fixing the office, etc.)?
- Lastly, what three small wins do you want to accomplish this week?

Week Twenty-Nine (Monday): List the ways that you are giving more value than any other primary care clinic in your area. Next to each one write why it is important to do each one.

_____
_____
_____
_____
_____
_____
_____
_____
_____
_____
_____
_____
_____
_____
_____
_____
_____
_____
_____
_____
_____

Week Twenty-Nine (Tuesday): What do you need to do to get back to the healthy, happy life you deserve and desire?

_____
_____
_____
_____
_____
_____
_____
_____
_____
_____
_____
_____
_____
_____
_____
_____
_____
_____
_____
_____
_____
_____

Week Twenty-Nine (Wednesday): What have you done recently to meet new people? Have you networked with local businesspeople? Neighbors? DPC docs? Sit down and write down new ways you can connect with others.

_____

_____

_____

_____

_____

_____

_____

_____

_____

_____

_____

_____

_____

_____

_____

_____

_____

_____

Week Twenty-Nine (Thursday): What have you learned as a DPC doctor/owner over the past year that you didn't expect? How has that helped you grow in your practice and as a person?

_____

_____

_____

_____

_____

_____

_____

_____

_____

_____

_____

_____

_____

_____

_____

_____

_____

_____

_____

Week Twenty-Nine (Friday): How can you become the most valuable person in your patients' lives? List some ways. Obviously, you give them peace of mind by being there for them as their doctor. Write that down. Anything else. Newsletters? Lectures?

_____

_____

_____

_____

_____

_____

_____

_____

_____

_____

_____

_____

_____

_____

_____

_____

_____

_____

Week Twenty-Nine (Saturday): How did the week go? Pick out things that went well. Did you help people? What did you accomplish? What could you have done even better? How about those three small wins you wrote down on Sunday? Did you accomplish them? Or just review what you wrote each day and put some of your thoughts down here.

_____

_____

_____

_____

_____

_____

_____

_____

_____

_____

_____

_____

_____

_____

_____

_____

_____

_____

_____

Week Thirty

Week Thirty (Sunday): It's time to plan your week again. Here are some things to think about, but feel free to only answer one or even something else entirely:

- What things can you do this week to become the doctor you've always wanted to be?
- What things can you do this week to work on your physical and mental self (working out, meditate, nature walks, sleep, reading, etc.)?
- What things can you do this week to improve your business (marketing, advertising, fixing the office, etc.)?
- Lastly, what three small wins do you want to accomplish this week?

Week Thirty (Monday): When do you feel the most overwhelmed, stressed, anxious or unhappy? Does this happen on a particular day or at a particular time of day? How can you switch your schedule to fix this?

_____
_____
_____
_____
_____
_____
_____
_____
_____
_____
_____
_____
_____
_____
_____
_____
_____
_____
_____

Week Thirty (Tuesday): How's your focus? Technology can be a great thing, but people are checking their phones 150 times a day. This breaks your focus and affects your thinking. Do you have techniques to monitor your technology use? Do you take planned breaks away from it? List ways you can do that.

_____
_____
_____
_____
_____
_____
_____
_____
_____
_____
_____
_____
_____
_____
_____
_____
_____
_____
_____
_____

Week Thirty (Wednesday): Write down some ways your job as a doctor makes a difference in the world. How does it make a difference in your patients' lives? How about your family members' lives?

_____

_____

_____

_____

_____

_____

_____

_____

_____

_____

_____

_____

_____

_____

_____

_____

_____

_____

Week Thirty (Thursday): What can you do today to make the experience for your office staff be better? They need to feel appreciated. If they are happy then your patients will be happy.

_____

_____

_____

_____

_____

_____

_____

_____

_____

_____

_____

_____

_____

_____

_____

_____

_____

Week Thirty (Friday): What podcasts or books can you listen to or read to improve yourself? Start investigating and list here. Search the "podcast" section on your phone or Google podcasts that may enrich your life. Do the same for books.   List here.

_____
_____
_____
_____
_____
_____
_____
_____
_____
_____
_____
_____
_____
_____
_____
_____
_____
_____

Week Thirty (Saturday): How did the week go? Pick out things that went well. Did you help people? What did you accomplish? What could you have done even better? How about those three small wins you wrote down on Sunday? Did you accomplish them?   Or just review what you wrote each day and put some of your thoughts down here.

_____
_____
_____
_____
_____
_____
_____
_____
_____
_____
_____
_____
_____
_____
_____
_____
_____
_____
_____

Week Thirty-One

Week Thirty-One (Sunday): It's time to plan your week again. Here are some things to think about, but feel free to only answer one or even something else entirely:

- What things can you do this week to become the doctor you've always wanted to be?
- What things can you do this week to work on your physical and mental self (working out, meditate, nature walks, sleep, reading, etc.)?
- What things can you do this week to improve your business (marketing, advertising, fixing the office, etc.)?
- Lastly, what three small wins do you want to accomplish this week?

_____
_____
_____
_____
_____
_____
_____
_____
_____
_____
_____
_____
_____
_____
_____
_____
_____
_____
_____
_____
_____
_____
_____
_____
_____
_____
_____
_____
_____
_____
_____

Week Thirty-One (Monday): The biggest bully you will ever meet is yourself. Write down some ways you have bullied yourself, been negative or berated yourself and why each one is not true or is over-exaggerated.

_____

_____

_____

_____

_____

_____

_____

_____

_____

_____

_____

_____

_____

_____

_____

_____

_____

_____

_____

_____

_____

Week Thirty-One (Tuesday): How would you describe yourself as a doctor? Are you happy with these answers? Is there room for improvement? How?

_____

_____

_____

_____

_____

_____

_____

_____

_____

_____

_____

_____

_____

_____

_____

_____

_____

_____

_____

_____

Week Thirty-One (Wednesday): Are you sleeping well? If not then what are some things you need to be doing to optimize your sleep (cutting blue light, better shades, etc.).

_____
_____
_____
_____
_____
_____
_____
_____
_____
_____
_____
_____
_____
_____
_____
_____
_____

Week Thirty-One (Thursday): All entrepreneurs need faith to succeed. It has been said that faith is the assurance of things of things hoped for and the conviction of things unseen. Think about this and list five to ten things you have faith in?

_____
_____
_____
_____
_____
_____
_____
_____
_____
_____
_____
_____
_____
_____
_____
_____
_____

Week Thirty-One (Friday): You need boundaries. What are they? For example, have you been abused by patients (bossed around, overused, have they treated your staff poorly, etc.). List new boundaries that you will strictly enforce and talk with your staff about them.

_____
_____
_____
_____
_____
_____
_____
_____
_____
_____
_____
_____
_____
_____
_____
_____

Week Thirty-One (Saturday): How did the week go? Pick out things that went well.   Did you help people? What did you accomplish? What could you have done even better? How about those three small wins you wrote down on Sunday? Did you accomplish them?   Or just review what you wrote each day and put some of your thoughts down here.

_____
_____
_____
_____
_____
_____
_____
_____
_____
_____
_____
_____
_____
_____
_____
_____
_____
_____

WEEK THIRTY-TWO

Week Thirty-Two (Sunday): It's time to plan your week again. Here are some things to think about, but feel free to only answer one or even something else entirely:

- What things can you do this week to become the doctor you've always wanted to be?
- What things can you do this week to work on your physical and mental self (working out, meditate, nature walks, sleep, reading, etc.)?
- What things can you do this week to improve your business (marketing, advertising, fixing the office, etc.)?
- Lastly, what three small wins do you want to accomplish this week?

Week Thirty-Two (Monday): What technology are you not using? List some things that you could at least experiment with to see if it adds value to your office or to patients.

_____
_____
_____
_____
_____
_____
_____
_____
_____
_____
_____
_____
_____
_____
_____
_____
_____
_____

Week Thirty-Two (Tuesday): What is the general population's pain points or anxieties with doctors? List your thoughts and why you and your office are different. This is a great pitch at a meet-and-greet by the way.

_____
_____
_____
_____
_____
_____
_____
_____
_____
_____
_____
_____
_____
_____
_____
_____
_____
_____
_____

Week Thirty-Two (Wednesday): What could happen in the office to make you feel great today? To make you feel at ease? To make you feel energized about your life calling?

_____
_____
_____
_____
_____
_____
_____
_____
_____
_____
_____
_____
_____
_____
_____
_____
_____
_____
_____
_____

Week Thirty-Two (Thursday): What is the number one investment you can make to move things exponentially forward in your life and business?

_____
_____
_____
_____
_____
_____
_____
_____
_____
_____
_____
_____
_____
_____
_____
_____
_____
_____
_____
_____
_____
_____

Week Thirty-Two (Friday): Have you rewarded yourself or your staff for your successes? It doesn't matter how small these rewards are. It can be just a reminder that you and your staff are working hard and that you deserve something. Name some small or big ways you can reward yourself and your staff.

_____
_____
_____
_____
_____
_____
_____
_____
_____
_____
_____
_____
_____
_____
_____
_____
_____
_____

Week Thirty-Two (Saturday): How did the week go? Pick out things that went well. Did you help people? What did you accomplish? What could you have done even better? How about those three small wins you wrote down on Sunday? Did you accomplish them? Or just review what you wrote each day and put some of your thoughts down here.

_____
_____
_____
_____
_____
_____
_____
_____
_____
_____
_____
_____
_____
_____
_____
_____
_____
_____
_____

WEEK THIRTY-THREE

Week Thirty-Three (Sunday): It's time to plan your week again. Here are some things to think about, but feel free to only answer one or even something else entirely:

- What things can you do this week to become the doctor you've always wanted to be?
- What things can you do this week to work on your physical and mental self (working out, meditate, nature walks, sleep, reading, etc.)?
- What things can you do this week to improve your business (marketing, advertising, fixing the office, etc.)?
- Lastly, what three small wins do you want to accomplish this week?

Week Thirty-Three (Monday): – What have you done to help others (out of the DPC world) recently? If you haven't done much, then what can you do?

_____
_____
_____
_____
_____
_____
_____
_____
_____
_____
_____
_____
_____
_____
_____
_____
_____

Week Thirty-Three (Tuesday): What's not excellent in your practice? List. How can you fix it or get rid of it?

_____
_____
_____
_____
_____
_____
_____
_____
_____
_____
_____
_____
_____
_____
_____
_____
_____
_____

Week Thirty-Three (Wednesday): What is the biggest issue you need to fix in your office right now? Now break it down and compartmentalize it into smaller pieces and list how you can fix those issues.

_____

_____

_____

_____

_____

_____

_____

_____

_____

_____

_____

_____

_____

_____

_____

_____

_____

_____

_____

Week Thirty-Three (Thursday): Are you reviewing records of patient before you see them? They want to know you know them personally. Ask them a personal question that proves it? If you don't know one, then start asking about their hobbies, their family, their jobs, etc. List ways you can make the job more personal yet still be professional.

_____

_____

_____

_____

_____

_____

_____

_____

_____

_____

_____

_____

_____

_____

_____

_____

_____

_____

Week Thirty-Three (Friday): What do you enjoy most about being a DPC doctor? What would need to change to make it even more enjoyable?

_____
_____
_____
_____
_____
_____
_____
_____
_____
_____
_____
_____
_____
_____
_____
_____
_____

Week Thirty-Three (Saturday): How did the week go? Pick out things that went well. Did you help people? What did you accomplish? What could you have done even better? How about those three small wins you wrote down on Sunday? Did you accomplish them? Or just review what you wrote each day and put some of your thoughts down here.

_____
_____
_____
_____
_____
_____
_____
_____
_____
_____
_____
_____
_____
_____
_____
_____

WEEK THIRTY-FOUR

Week Thirty-Four (Sunday): It's time to plan your week again. Here are some things to think about, but feel free to only answer one or even something else entirely:

- What things can you do this week to become the doctor you've always wanted to be?
- What things can you do this week to work on your physical and mental self (working out, meditate, nature walks, sleep, reading, etc.)?
- What things can you do this week to improve your business (marketing, advertising, fixing the office, etc.)?
- Lastly, what three small wins do you want to accomplish this week?

Week Thirty-Four (Monday): You will make mistakes. That is life. List some of the mistakes you made while building your practice (let your ego go) and then what you have done to correct them.

_____

Week Thirty-Four (Tuesday): What are your new goals for the practice: increasing the number of patients, expanding your practice, providing new value services?

_____

Week Thirty-Four (Wednesday): What can you do to create a happier patient and a more friction-free experience at the office?

_____
_____
_____
_____
_____
_____
_____
_____
_____
_____
_____
_____
_____
_____
_____
_____
_____

Week Thirty-Four (Thursday): What can you do today that you couldn't do a year ago? For example, run a practice or pitch a businessperson on what you offer. List some more.

_____
_____
_____
_____
_____
_____
_____
_____
_____
_____
_____
_____
_____
_____
_____
_____
_____
_____

Week Thirty-Four (Friday): Which life skill can you work on? Remembering names? Reading a book a week? Learning a new workout routine? List some ideas and action plans.

_____
_____
_____
_____
_____
_____
_____
_____
_____
_____
_____
_____
_____
_____
_____
_____
_____
_____

Week Thirty-Four (Saturday): How did the week go? Pick out things that went well.   Did you help people? What did you accomplish? What could you have done even better? How about those three small wins you wrote down on Sunday? Did you accomplish them?   Or just review what you wrote each day and put some of your thoughts down here.

_____
_____
_____
_____
_____
_____
_____
_____
_____
_____
_____
_____
_____
_____
_____
_____
_____
_____

WEEK THIRTY-FIVE

Week Thirty-Five (Sunday): It's time to plan your week again. Here are some things to think about, but feel free to only answer one or even something else entirely:

- What things can you do this week to become the doctor you've always wanted to be?
- What things can you do this week to work on your physical and mental self (working out, meditate, nature walks, sleep, reading, etc.)?
- What things can you do this week to improve your business (marketing, advertising, fixing the office, etc.)?
- Lastly, what three small wins do you want to accomplish this week?

Week Thirty-Five (Monday): Learn to let go. There are some patients who will never be satisfied, who will criticize you when they leave, and who will make you feel terrible. List some ways you WON'T take it personally. For example, "it happens to all DPC docs" or "I will forgive them". Little tip here, NEVER email them, argue or debate with them why about why they left the practice. Let go.

_____
_____
_____
_____
_____
_____
_____
_____
_____
_____
_____
_____
_____
_____
_____
_____
_____
_____
_____

Week Thirty-Five (Tuesday): What things are you doing to physically and mentally take care of yourself? Are you in good shape? How is your diet? How is your sleep? How can you improve these things? You always have to walk your talk.

_____
_____
_____
_____
_____
_____
_____
_____
_____
_____
_____
_____
_____
_____
_____
_____
_____
_____
_____

Week Thirty-Five (Wednesday): What big ideas do you have for the DPC industry? Pretend you had the ear of the government or you had a magic wand. How would you change things with DPC or the healthcare system? Dream big here. Take some time and list them.

_____

_____

_____

_____

_____

_____

_____

_____

_____

_____

_____

_____

_____

_____

_____

_____

_____

_____

Week Thirty-Five (Thursday): What can you do to reduce costs in your practice? What are areas you can put more capital into?

_____

_____

_____

_____

_____

_____

_____

_____

_____

_____

_____

_____

_____

_____

_____

_____

_____

_____

Week Thirty-Five (Friday): Where are you winning in life or on the DPC job? Brag a little here. Is it less stress? Is it more connections to patients? More income?

_____

_____

_____

_____

_____

_____

_____

_____

_____

_____

_____

_____

_____

_____

_____

_____

_____

_____

_____

Week Thirty-Five (Saturday): How did the week go? Pick out things that went well.   Did you help people? What did you accomplish? What could you have done even better? How about those three small wins you wrote down on Sunday? Did you accomplish them?   Or just review what you wrote each day and put some of your thoughts down here.

_____

_____

_____

_____

_____

_____

_____

_____

_____

_____

_____

_____

_____

_____

_____

_____

_____

WEEK THIRTY-SIX

Week Thirty-Six (Sunday): It's time to plan your week again. Here are some things to think about, but feel free to only answer one or even something else entirely:

- What things can you do this week to become the doctor you've always wanted to be?
- What things can you do this week to work on your physical and mental self (working out, meditate, nature walks, sleep, reading, etc.)?
- What things can you do this week to improve your business (marketing, advertising, fixing the office, etc.)?
- Lastly, what three small wins do you want to accomplish this week?

Week Thirty-Six (Monday): What can you do to experience more peace and freedom in your life?

_____
_____
_____
_____
_____
_____
_____
_____
_____
_____
_____
_____
_____
_____
_____
_____
_____
_____
_____
_____

Week Thirty-Six (Tuesday): What did you do that was fun or made you happy recently? If nothing, what could you be doing? It doesn't even have to be related to the practice. It could just be in life.

_____
_____
_____
_____
_____
_____
_____
_____
_____
_____
_____
_____
_____
_____
_____
_____
_____
_____
_____

Week Thirty-Six (Wednesday): What is the next level for you in your practice? Define it any way you want. How can you get there?

_____
_____
_____
_____
_____
_____
_____
_____
_____
_____
_____
_____
_____
_____
_____
_____
_____
_____
_____

Week Thirty-Six (Thursday): Compared to what you were a year or even 5 years ago, how have your improved as a person? How about as a doctor?

_____
_____
_____
_____
_____
_____
_____
_____
_____
_____
_____
_____
_____
_____
_____
_____
_____
_____
_____

Week Thirty-Six (Friday): You will always have times when you struggle. Name some things you can do to get unstuck and to free yourself when they happen.

_____
_____
_____
_____
_____
_____
_____
_____
_____
_____
_____
_____
_____
_____
_____
_____
_____
_____

Week Thirty-Six (Saturday): How did the week go? Pick out things that went well. Did you help people? What did you accomplish? What could you have done even better? How about those three small wins you wrote down on Sunday? Did you accomplish them? Or just review what you wrote each day and put some of your thoughts down here.

_____
_____
_____
_____
_____
_____
_____
_____
_____
_____
_____
_____
_____
_____
_____
_____
_____
_____
_____
_____

WEEK THIRTY-SEVEN

Week Thirty-Seven (Sunday): It's time to plan your week again. Here are some things to think about, but feel free to only answer one or even something else entirely:

- What things can you do this week to become the doctor you've always wanted to be?
- What things can you do this week to work on your physical and mental self (working out, meditate, nature walks, sleep, reading, etc.)?
- What things can you do this week to improve your business (marketing, advertising, fixing the office, etc.)?
- Lastly, what three small wins do you want to accomplish this week?

Week Thirty-Seven (Monday): What kind of message can you craft to get your ideal patient and stand out from any competitors?

_____
_____
_____
_____
_____
_____
_____
_____
_____
_____
_____
_____
_____
_____
_____
_____
_____
_____

Week Thirty-Seven (Tuesday): Let's address the Pareto Principle again but in this way. Aobut 80% of your work comes from 20% of your patients. List the names or initials of those patients. How can you stop them from burdening you? For example, you can fire them or you can schedule them monthly in perpetuity. Both are examples of what some DPC docs do. In either case, make a plan to make your life easier.

_____
_____
_____
_____
_____
_____
_____
_____
_____
_____
_____
_____
_____
_____
_____
_____
_____
_____

Week Thirty-Seven (Wednesday): How would you define success? What would have to happen for you to meet that definition?

_____

_____

_____

_____

_____

_____

_____

_____

_____

_____

_____

_____

_____

_____

_____

_____

_____

_____

_____

_____

Week Thirty-Seven (Thursday): They say the bigger the "why" then the easier the "how"? Why does your DPC practice need to be successful for you, for your family, for you patients? This will push you to figure out the how and then how to make it happen.

_____

_____

_____

_____

_____

_____

_____

_____

_____

_____

_____

_____

_____

_____

_____

_____

_____

_____

_____

Week Thirty-Seven (Friday): What are some of the things you do to relax each day? List them and list others you would consider doing.

_____

_____

_____

_____

_____

_____

_____

_____

_____

_____

_____

_____

_____

_____

_____

_____

_____

_____

Week Thirty-Seven (Saturday): How did the week go? Pick out things that went well.   Did you help people? What did you accomplish? What could you have done even better? How about those three small wins you wrote down on Sunday? Did you accomplish them?   Or just review what you wrote each day and put some of your thoughts down here.

_____

_____

_____

_____

_____

_____

_____

_____

_____

_____

_____

_____

_____

_____

_____

_____

_____

_____

_____

WEEK THIRTY-EIGHT

Week Thirty-Eight (Sunday): It's time to plan your week again. Here are some things to think about, but feel free to only answer one or even something else entirely:

- What things can you do this week to become the doctor you've always wanted to be?
- What things can you do this week to work on your physical and mental self (working out, meditate, nature walks, sleep, reading, etc.)?
- What things can you do this week to improve your business (marketing, advertising, fixing the office, etc.)?
- Lastly, what three small wins do you want to accomplish this week?

Week Thirty-Eight (Monday): Don't get complacent and fall in love with yourself too much. What are areas you may be slipping up in the practice or be taking for granted? For example, following up with patients? Marketing? Remember, marketing is important to protect your brand even if you are filled. List some weak spots and some ways you can work on them.

Week Thirty-Eight (Tuesday): What are your best personal qualities in life and how do they benefit your practice?

Week Thirty-Eight (Wednesday): Are your patients not only leaving feeling satisfied but also happy? Do they brag about you? If so, what do you think they are bragging about? If not, what needs to change?

_____

_____

_____

_____

_____

_____

_____

_____

_____

_____

_____

_____

_____

_____

_____

_____

_____

Week Thirty-Eight (Thursday): What are you committed to getting done in your practice over the next month, three months, six months or year? Time to reflect and plan again.

_____

_____

_____

_____

_____

_____

_____

_____

_____

_____

_____

_____

_____

_____

_____

_____

_____

_____

_____

Week Thirty-Eight (Friday): What are you biggest strengths as a DPC doctor? How can you utilize them more to help patients or to grow your practice?

_____
_____
_____
_____
_____
_____
_____
_____
_____
_____
_____
_____
_____
_____
_____
_____
_____
_____

Week Thirty-Eight (Saturday): How did the week go? Pick out things that went well. Did you help people? What did you accomplish? What could you have done even better? How about those three small wins you wrote down on Sunday? Did you accomplish them? Or just review what you wrote each day and put some of your thoughts down here.

_____
_____
_____
_____
_____
_____
_____
_____
_____
_____
_____
_____
_____
_____
_____
_____
_____

WEEK THIRTY-NINE

Week Thirty-Nine (Sunday): It's time to plan your week again. Here are some things to think about, but feel free to only answer one or even something else entirely:

- What things can you do this week to become the doctor you've always wanted to be?
- What things can you do this week to work on your physical and mental self (working out, meditate, nature walks, sleep, reading, etc.)?
- What things can you do this week to improve your business (marketing, advertising, fixing the office, etc.)?
- Lastly, what three small wins do you want to accomplish this week?

Week Thirty-Nine (Monday): List some examples of when you have truly helped patients over the last week or month. Use patient initials. You need these moments to prove to yourself how much good you are doing in the world.

_____
_____
_____
_____
_____
_____
_____
_____
_____
_____
_____
_____
_____
_____
_____
_____
_____
_____
_____

Week Thirty-Nine (Tuesday): Big things come from lots of success in the little things. You need to be great in those little things. What little things are you doing or could you be doing regularly?

_____
_____
_____
_____
_____
_____
_____
_____
_____
_____
_____
_____
_____
_____
_____
_____
_____
_____
_____

Week Thirty-Nine (Wednesday): What is it about being a family doctor or DPC doctor are you most thankful for? List and say why.

_____

_____

_____

_____

_____

_____

_____

_____

_____

_____

_____

_____

_____

_____

_____

_____

_____

_____

Week Thirty-Nine (Thursday): What can you change about yourself to make yourself a better businessperson? Yes, businessperson.   Can you learn how to invest?   Can you learn about giving better service? List some ideas.

_____

_____

_____

_____

_____

_____

_____

_____

_____

_____

_____

_____

_____

_____

_____

_____

_____

Week Thirty-Nine (Friday): Go back and think about the past week. When did you feel very energized, engaged and motivated? What caused this? Was it something you did or didn't do? Maybe it was your diet? Fun things? Great patients? List them. When you see a pattern, then do what it takes to have more of those moments.

_____

_____

_____

_____

_____

_____

_____

_____

_____

_____

_____

_____

_____

_____

_____

_____

Week Thirty-Nine (Saturday): How did the week go? Pick out things that went well. Did you help people? What did you accomplish? What could you have done even better? How about those three small wins you wrote down on Sunday? Did you accomplish them? Or just review what you wrote each day and put some of your thoughts down here.

_____

_____

_____

_____

_____

_____

_____

_____

_____

_____

_____

_____

_____

_____

_____

_____

WEEK FORTY

Week Forty (Sunday): It's time to plan your week again. Here are some things to think about, but feel free to only answer one or even something else entirely:

- What things can you do this week to become the doctor you've always wanted to be?
- What things can you do this week to work on your physical and mental self (working out, meditate, nature walks, sleep, reading, etc.)?
- What things can you do this week to improve your business (marketing, advertising, fixing the office, etc.)?
- Lastly, what three small wins do you want to accomplish this week?

Week Forty (Monday): What makes you your own thing? What makes you unique, special, or different? How has that helped you in the past? How can you use that to be the best DPC doc you can be?

_____

_____

_____

_____

_____

_____

_____

_____

_____

_____

_____

_____

_____

_____

_____

_____

_____

_____

Week Forty (Tuesday): What setbacks have you had since you started your DPC practice? List ways you would change things next time or what you would tell a prospective doctor to do if he or she was starting a DPC practice? What would you do differently next time?

_____

_____

_____

_____

_____

_____

_____

_____

_____

_____

_____

_____

_____

_____

_____

_____

_____

_____

Week Forty (Wednesday): What are you most excited about in life or in your practice right now? Time to just let it flow and write.

_____

_____

_____

_____

_____

_____

_____

_____

_____

_____

_____

_____

_____

_____

_____

_____

_____

_____

_____

Week Forty (Thursday): Remember, this is your practice. Do you feel overwhelmed? Are there situations where if you could go back in time you would change something? List some ways you can take control over your practice in these situations.

_____

_____

_____

_____

_____

_____

_____

_____

_____

_____

_____

_____

_____

_____

_____

_____

_____

_____

_____

_____

Week Forty (Friday): Sometimes we get mixed messages. They say don't sweat the small stuff, but someone in your office has to. What is the small stuff that needs sweating over in your DPC practice? Can you delegate some of those things to others or should you take care of them? Make a list with a name attached to each item.

_____

_____

_____

_____

_____

_____

_____

_____

_____

_____

_____

_____

_____

_____

_____

_____

_____

Week Forty (Saturday): How did the week go? Pick out things that went well. Did you help people? What did you accomplish? What could you have done even better? How about those three small wins you wrote down on Sunday? Did you accomplish them? Or just review what you wrote each day and put some of your thoughts down here.

_____

_____

_____

_____

_____

_____

_____

_____

_____

_____

_____

_____

_____

_____

_____

_____

_____

_____

_____

WEEK FORTY-ONE

Week Forty-One (Sunday): It's time to plan your week again. Here are some things to think about, but feel free to only answer one or even something else entirely:

- What things can you do this week to become the doctor you've always wanted to be?
- What things can you do this week to work on your physical and mental self (working out, meditate, nature walks, sleep, reading, etc.)?
- What things can you do this week to improve your business (marketing, advertising, fixing the office, etc.)?
- Lastly, what three small wins do you want to accomplish this week?

Week Forty-One (Monday): Use this day to say thank you or to appreciate someone in your world. List people you could say this to or you could at least email or text.

_____
_____
_____
_____
_____
_____
_____
_____
_____
_____
_____
_____
_____
_____
_____
_____
_____
_____
_____

Week Forty-One (Tuesday): What is the one skill you could learn that would your practice to the next level? For example, is it marketing, public speaking, or leadership? The secret, as Brian Tracy says, is that all skills are learnable. They may not be fun or easy but they are learnable. List the skills that you need, pick the most important one and then learn it.

_____
_____
_____
_____
_____
_____
_____
_____
_____
_____
_____
_____
_____
_____
_____
_____
_____
_____

Week Forty-One (Wednesday): You are being watched from the moment you see a patient. Did you know that? Knowing this, what could you do better at? Clothing? Your greeting?

_____
_____
_____
_____
_____
_____
_____
_____
_____
_____
_____
_____
_____
_____
_____
_____
_____
_____
_____

Week Forty-One (Thursday): What is an example recently where you persevered through some adversity? How did that make you feel?

_____
_____
_____
_____
_____
_____
_____
_____
_____
_____
_____
_____
_____
_____
_____
_____
_____
_____
_____

Week Forty-One (Friday): What innovative ways can you get the word out about what you do? Remember, you still need to be getting patients interested in what you are doing. If you are not filled, then you need patients. If you are filled, then you always need a waiting list.

_____
_____
_____
_____
_____
_____
_____
_____
_____
_____
_____
_____
_____
_____
_____
_____
_____

Week Forty-One (Saturday): How did the week go? Pick out things that went well. Did you help people? What did you accomplish? What could you have done even better? How about those three small wins you wrote down on Sunday? Did you accomplish them? Or just review what you wrote each day and put some of your thoughts down here.

_____
_____
_____
_____
_____
_____
_____
_____
_____
_____
_____
_____
_____
_____
_____
_____
_____
_____

WEEK FORTY-TWO

Week Forty-Two (Sunday): It's time to plan your week again. Here are some things to think about, but feel free to only answer one or even something else entirely:

- What things can you do this week to become the doctor you've always wanted to be?
- What things can you do this week to work on your physical and mental self (working out, meditate, nature walks, sleep, reading, etc.)?
- What things can you do this week to improve your business (marketing, advertising, fixing the office, etc.)?
- Lastly, what three small wins do you want to accomplish this week?

_____
_____
_____
_____
_____
_____
_____
_____
_____
_____
_____
_____
_____
_____
_____
_____
_____
_____
_____
_____
_____
_____
_____
_____
_____
_____
_____
_____
_____
_____

Week Forty-Two (Monday): What do you stand for in life? This is a very general question, but think it about it and start writing.

_____
_____
_____
_____
_____
_____
_____
_____
_____
_____
_____
_____
_____
_____
_____
_____
_____
_____

Week Forty-Two (Tuesday): What's the best part of your DPC job? What's the worst? How can you add more of the former and remove the latter?

_____
_____
_____
_____
_____
_____
_____
_____
_____
_____
_____
_____
_____
_____
_____
_____
_____
_____

Week Forty-Two (Wednesday): To be successful you need to build a DPC practice that people love so much they tell everyone about it. Is your practice giving them that experience? If not, what would that experience look like? If yes, what factors are contributing to creating that experience? Another way to look at is if Steve Jobs or Walt Disney were in charge of your practice, how would they make the experience better?

_____
_____
_____
_____
_____
_____
_____
_____
_____
_____
_____
_____
_____
_____
_____
_____
_____

Week Forty-Two (Thursday): What kind of doctor do your really want to be? Think back to when you first wanted to be a doctor. Can you remember what your dream was then? What did you think your office would look like? Is what you're doing now close to that dream? What changes can you make to move in that direction?

_____
_____
_____
_____
_____
_____
_____
_____
_____
_____
_____
_____
_____
_____
_____
_____
_____
_____

Week Forty-Two (Friday): Are you following up with patients? Just a quick email to check on them would be great. Be careful. Your frequent flyers may abuse this and may start volleying emails back to you. How else can you follow up with patients? Thanking them for referrals? Checking on their illnesses, their recent important life events, etc.? Brainstorm some ideas.

_____
_____
_____
_____
_____
_____
_____
_____
_____
_____
_____
_____
_____
_____
_____
_____

Week Forty-Two (Saturday): How did the week go? Pick out things that went well. Did you help people? What did you accomplish? What could you have done even better? How about those three small wins you wrote down on Sunday? Did you accomplish them? Or just review what you wrote each day and put some of your thoughts down here.

_____
_____
_____
_____
_____
_____
_____
_____
_____
_____
_____
_____
_____
_____
_____
_____
_____
_____

WEEK FORTY-THREE

Week Forty-Three (Sunday): It's time to plan your week again. Here are some things to think about, but feel free to only answer one or even something else entirely:

- What things can you do this week to become the doctor you've always wanted to be?
- What things can you do this week to work on your physical and mental self (working out, meditate, nature walks, sleep, reading, etc.)?
- What things can you do this week to improve your business (marketing, advertising, fixing the office, etc.)?
- Lastly, what three small wins do you want to accomplish this week?

Week Forty-Three (Monday): Your mind is always racing and trying to find answers. What can you do to give it a rest? Meditate? Exercise? Have you blown this off? Don't. Walk in nature. Go to a movie. Rest your noggin (after you brainstorm this question of course). Plan a time each this week to do something and follow through. List some things you can do.

_____
_____
_____
_____
_____
_____
_____
_____
_____
_____
_____
_____
_____
_____
_____
_____
_____
_____

Week Forty-Three (Tuesday): Be proud of what you do? You help people. You change lives. List some other ways you are proud of yourself. Brag. No one else will see this but you.

_____
_____
_____
_____
_____
_____
_____
_____
_____
_____
_____
_____
_____
_____
_____
_____
_____
_____
_____
_____
_____

Week Forty-Three (Wednesday): What do you hate about what you do? What do you love about what you do? Don't feel bad if you still have a ton of answers for the former. It is therapeutic just to write them out.

_____
_____
_____
_____
_____
_____
_____
_____
_____
_____
_____
_____
_____
_____
_____
_____
_____
_____

Week Forty-Three (Thursday): How do you want to be remembered for after you retire from being a doctor? It seems simple, but how do you want your patients to talk about you?

_____
_____
_____
_____
_____
_____
_____
_____
_____
_____
_____
_____
_____
_____
_____
_____
_____
_____

Week Forty-Three (Friday): What are you thankful for in life, even if it is not perfect?

Week Forty-Three (Saturday): How did the week go? Pick out things that went well. Did you help people? What did you accomplish? What could you have done even better? How about those three small wins you wrote down on Sunday? Did you accomplish them? Or just review what you wrote each day and put some of your thoughts down here.

WEEK FORTY-FOUR

Week Forty-Four (Sunday): It's time to plan your week again. Here are some things to think about, but feel free to only answer one or even something else entirely:

- What things can you do this week to become the doctor you've always wanted to be?
- What things can you do this week to work on your physical and mental self (working out, meditate, nature walks, sleep, reading, etc.)?
- What things can you do this week to improve your business (marketing, advertising, fixing the office, etc.)?
- Lastly, what three small wins do you want to accomplish this week?

Week Forty-Four (Monday): Being a great physician is critical to your future, your success and your self-esteem. What are you presently doing to be master of your craft?

_____
_____
_____
_____
_____
_____
_____
_____
_____
_____
_____
_____
_____
_____
_____
_____
_____
_____
_____

Week Forty-Four (Tuesday): What do you appreciate about your practice, your staff and your patients?

_____
_____
_____
_____
_____
_____
_____
_____
_____
_____
_____
_____
_____
_____
_____
_____
_____
_____
_____
_____

Week Forty-Four (Wednesday): Why do you get up in the morning? Why do you go to work every day?

_____
_____
_____
_____
_____
_____
_____
_____
_____
_____
_____
_____
_____
_____
_____
_____
_____
_____

Week Forty-Four (Thursday): So how is your job? More importantly, are you enjoying the journey? Which parts? Name some struggles and victories you can be proud of.

_____
_____
_____
_____
_____
_____
_____
_____
_____
_____
_____
_____
_____
_____
_____
_____
_____
_____
_____
_____
_____

Week Forty-Four (Friday): Don't forget to work on your own personal stuff. DPC is great and all, but list some things you may be neglecting that need to be turned around. For example, relationships with family, connecting with friends, your health status, etc. What are some things you could do to strengthen these areas?

_____

_____

_____

_____

_____

_____

_____

_____

_____

_____

_____

_____

_____

_____

_____

_____

Week Forty-Four (Saturday): How did the week go? Pick out things that went well.   Did you help people? What did you accomplish? What could you have done even better? How about those three small wins you wrote down on Sunday? Did you accomplish them?   Or just review what you wrote each day and put some of your thoughts down here.

_____

_____

_____

_____

_____

_____

_____

_____

_____

_____

_____

_____

_____

_____

_____

_____

_____

WEEK FORTY-FIVE

Week Forty-Five (Sunday): It's time to plan your week again. Here are some things to think about, but feel free to only answer one or even something else entirely:

- What things can you do this week to become the doctor you've always wanted to be?
- What things can you do this week to work on your physical and mental self (working out, meditate, nature walks, sleep, reading, etc.)?
- What things can you do this week to improve your business (marketing, advertising, fixing the office, etc.)?
- Lastly, what three small wins do you want to accomplish this week?

Week Forty-Five (Monday): We all have "To Do" lists. Now make a "Not To Do" list. Put down all those things that you shouldn't do which affect your progress. Examples can be "don't keep checking your phone" or "don't negatively talk about yourself," etc.

_____

_____

_____

_____

_____

_____

_____

_____

_____

_____

_____

_____

_____

_____

_____

_____

_____

_____

Week Forty-Five (Tuesday): Imagine yourself at your best. What does that look like? What are you wearing? How is your eye contact? How is you posture? How is your confidence?

_____

_____

_____

_____

_____

_____

_____

_____

_____

_____

_____

_____

_____

_____

_____

_____

_____

_____

_____

Week Forty-Five (Wednesday): What are the top 5 most important priorities in your life right now?

_____
_____
_____
_____
_____
_____
_____
_____
_____
_____
_____
_____
_____
_____
_____
_____
_____
_____

Week Forty-Five (Thursday): In what ways are you indispensible to your patients? Are there other ways you can be more indispensible? List them.

_____
_____
_____
_____
_____
_____
_____
_____
_____
_____
_____
_____
_____
_____
_____
_____
_____

Week Forty-Five (Friday): You will never be good enough for some patients. That is just a reality. Even the ones who loved you, may fire you some day. Can you learn from it? Sure. More importantly, though, write down some of the ways you have done the best you can for your patients? For example, I am always honest or I truly care about their issues, etc.

_____
_____
_____
_____
_____
_____
_____
_____
_____
_____
_____
_____
_____
_____
_____
_____

Week Forty-Five (Saturday): How did the week go? Pick out things that went well. Did you help people? What did you accomplish? What could you have done even better? How about those three small wins you wrote down on Sunday? Did you accomplish them? Or just review what you wrote each day and put some of your thoughts down here.

_____
_____
_____
_____
_____
_____
_____
_____
_____
_____
_____
_____
_____
_____
_____
_____

WEEK FORTY-SIX

Week Forty-Six (Sunday): It's time to plan your week again. Here are some things to think about, but feel free to only answer one or even something else entirely:

- What things can you do this week to become the doctor you've always wanted to be?
- What things can you do this week to work on your physical and mental self (working out, meditate, nature walks, sleep, reading, etc.)?
- What things can you do this week to improve your business (marketing, advertising, fixing the office, etc.)?
- Lastly, what three small wins do you want to accomplish this week?

Week Forty-Six (Monday): You are not a perfect person. Therefore, you will not be a perfect doctor or businessperson. What are you flaws? List them. What can you change, embrace, share and laugh about?

_____

_____

_____

_____

_____

_____

_____

_____

_____

_____

_____

_____

_____

_____

_____

_____

_____

Week Forty-Six (Tuesday): Which patients are you grateful for? The overwhelming majority are great people. Using initials, write down a few and state why it awesome to see them or how great it is to help them.

_____

_____

_____

_____

_____

_____

_____

_____

_____

_____

_____

_____

_____

_____

_____

_____

_____

_____

_____

_____

Week Forty-Six (Wednesday): Sometimes you need to be uncomfortable in life to break out of a rut, create new habits or come up with new ideas. Some people do simple things like trying a new breakfast, going out to a play you would never usually go to, taking a trip to place you never thought of going or even doing a new exercise you never thought you would get caught doing. List some things you can do to be uncomfortable in your life.

_____

_____

_____

_____

_____

_____

_____

_____

_____

_____

_____

_____

_____

_____

_____

_____

_____

Week Forty-Six (Thursday): What habits or rituals are you doing each morning to prepare for your day. List them. Not many? What can you add? Reading, meditating, writing in this journal, etc.

_____

_____

_____

_____

_____

_____

_____

_____

_____

_____

_____

_____

_____

_____

_____

_____

_____

_____

_____

_____

Week Forty-Six (Friday): What is your ambition in life? Is it unique? Is there anything else you want to accomplish? Don't hold back. Think big! You can always pare back later.

_____

_____

_____

_____

_____

_____

_____

_____

_____

_____

_____

_____

_____

_____

_____

_____

_____

Week Forty-Six (Saturday): How did the week go? Pick out things that went well.   Did you help people? What did you accomplish? What could you have done even better? How about those three small wins you wrote down on Sunday? Did you accomplish them?   Or just review what you wrote each day and put some of your thoughts down here.

_____

_____

_____

_____

_____

_____

_____

_____

_____

_____

_____

_____

_____

_____

_____

_____

_____

WEEK FORTY-SEVEN

Week Forty-Seven (Sunday): It's time to plan your week again. Here are some things to think about, but feel free to only answer one or even something else entirely:

- What things can you do this week to become the doctor you've always wanted to be?
- What things can you do this week to work on your physical and mental self (working out, meditate, nature walks, sleep, reading, etc.)?
- What things can you do this week to improve your business (marketing, advertising, fixing the office, etc.)?
- Lastly, what three small wins do you want to accomplish this week?

Week Forty-Seven (Monday): What in your practice or in your day could you do without? Some things are just habits but are unessential. Think of some things you could remove and try to remove them because they are wasting your time. Brainstorm now but also keep a running list.

_____
_____
_____
_____
_____
_____
_____
_____
_____
_____
_____
_____
_____
_____
_____
_____
_____
_____
_____

Week Forty-Seven (Tuesday): Are you giving enough to each visit? List some things you can also do. For example, share something personal or ask about a prior illness or ask about a relative.

_____
_____
_____
_____
_____
_____
_____
_____
_____
_____
_____
_____
_____
_____
_____
_____
_____
_____
_____
_____
_____
_____

Week Forty-Seven (Wednesday): Now that you are a DPC doctor, what ways are you in more control over your life? Look at some things inside your practice as well as your home and personal life.

_____
_____
_____
_____
_____
_____
_____
_____
_____
_____
_____
_____
_____
_____
_____
_____
_____
_____

Week Forty-Seven (Thursday): Time to celebrate something about your office again? Is there another milestone you can celebrate about the staff, how many patients you have, being out of debt, etc.?

_____
_____
_____
_____
_____
_____
_____
_____
_____
_____
_____
_____
_____
_____
_____
_____
_____
_____
_____
_____

Week Forty-Seven (Friday): Look at your schedule. What do you want to spend more time doing? What do you want to spend less time doing?

_____
_____
_____
_____
_____
_____
_____
_____
_____
_____
_____
_____
_____
_____
_____
_____
_____
_____
_____

Week Forty-Seven (Saturday): How did the week go? Pick out things that went well. Did you help people? What did you accomplish? What could you have done even better? How about those three small wins you wrote down on Sunday? Did you accomplish them? Or just review what you wrote each day and put some of your thoughts down here.

_____
_____
_____
_____
_____
_____
_____
_____
_____
_____
_____
_____
_____
_____
_____
_____
_____
_____
_____
_____

WEEK FORTY-EIGHT

Week Forty-Eight (Sunday): It's time to plan your week again. Here are some things to think about, but feel free to only answer one or even something else entirely:

- What things can you do this week to become the doctor you've always wanted to be?
- What things can you do this week to work on your physical and mental self (working out, meditate, nature walks, sleep, reading, etc.)?
- What things can you do this week to improve your business (marketing, advertising, fixing the office, etc.)?
- Lastly, what three small wins do you want to accomplish this week?

Week Forty-Eight (Monday): Are there are still parts of your job that you hate doing? List them. Do you have to do them? Can you eliminate them or delegate them?

_____
_____
_____
_____
_____
_____
_____
_____
_____
_____
_____
_____
_____
_____
_____
_____
_____
_____

Week Forty-Eight (Tuesday): What personal passion projects are you working on? Don't have any? List some things you've always wanted to do. Travel? Sing? Do stand-up comedy?

_____
_____
_____
_____
_____
_____
_____
_____
_____
_____
_____
_____
_____
_____
_____
_____
_____
_____
_____

Week Forty-Eight (Wednesday): What are some of the things that keep you awake at night? Let it out here and comment on ways to fix them. Your sleep and your sanity are critical to your health and wellbeing.

_____
_____
_____
_____
_____
_____
_____
_____
_____
_____
_____
_____
_____
_____
_____
_____
_____
_____

Week Forty-Eight (Thursday): What are some habits or things you do that you should unlearn? It could be something as simple as sitting too long during the day. Or maybe eating lunch at your desk instead of getting out and eating somewhere else or maybe it is just going for a walk. List them and state why you should unlearn them.

_____
_____
_____
_____
_____
_____
_____
_____
_____
_____
_____
_____
_____
_____
_____
_____

Week Forty-Eight (Friday): What are some of your life's defining moments? What are those moments that made you who you are? List them here and how you grew from them.

Week Forty-Eight (Saturday): How did the week go? Pick out things that went well. Did you help people? What did you accomplish? What could you have done even better? How about those three small wins you wrote down on Sunday? Did you accomplish them? Or just review what you wrote each day and put some of your thoughts down here.

WEEK FORTY-NINE

Week Forty-Nine (Sunday): It's time to plan your week again. Here are some things to think about, but feel free to only answer one or even something else entirely:

- What things can you do this week to become the doctor you've always wanted to be?
- What things can you do this week to work on your physical and mental self (working out, meditate, nature walks, sleep, reading, etc.)?
- What things can you do this week to improve your business (marketing, advertising, fixing the office, etc.)?
- Lastly, what three small wins do you want to accomplish this week?

Week Forty-Nine (Monday): What do you have to look forward to this week in your practice? How about in your life?

_____

_____

_____

_____

_____

_____

_____

_____

_____

_____

_____

_____

_____

_____

_____

_____

_____

_____

_____

Week Forty-Nine (Tuesday): Do you take time to breathe? Take enough time to spend with patients? To relax? To care? Life is not a sprint. DPC is not a sprint. Write down how you need to slow down, to relax more, to breathe more, to care more and other positive affirmations in this area.

_____

_____

_____

_____

_____

_____

_____

_____

_____

_____

_____

_____

_____

_____

_____

_____

_____

_____

_____

_____

Week Forty-Nine (Wednesday): What opportunities in life should you take advantage of? This may be in the medical field, but it should include some things outside of healthcare.

_____

_____

_____

_____

_____

_____

_____

_____

_____

_____

_____

_____

_____

_____

_____

_____

_____

_____

_____

Week Forty-Nine (Thursday): Starbucks is constantly finding ways to cater to their clients. Are you? How could you do more of this so that word of mouth spreads?

_____

_____

_____

_____

_____

_____

_____

_____

_____

_____

_____

_____

_____

_____

_____

_____

Week Forty-Nine (Friday): Are you still hungry to be the best? Are you still going the extra mile for your patients and staff? If no, then list what you can do. If yes, then prove it by listing those things you are doing.

Week Forty-Nine (Saturday): How did the week go? Pick out things that went well. Did you help people? What did you accomplish? What could you have done even better? How about those three small wins you wrote down on Sunday? Did you accomplish them? Or just review what you wrote each day and put some of your thoughts down here.

WEEK FIFTY

Week Fifty (Sunday): It's time to plan your week again. Here are some things to think about, but feel free to only answer one or even something else entirely:

- What things can you do this week to become the doctor you've always wanted to be?
- What things can you do this week to work on your physical and mental self (working out, meditate, nature walks, sleep, reading, etc.)?
- What things can you do this week to improve your business (marketing, advertising, fixing the office, etc.)?
- Lastly, what three small wins do you want to accomplish this week?

Week Fifty (Monday): Politics is no fun, but it is sometimes a part of DPC. How can you be more engaged in this process? Have you contacted your Congressman? Have you gone to DC to do some lobbying with other DPC docs? List some ideas on how you can be more involved.

_____
_____
_____
_____
_____
_____
_____
_____
_____
_____
_____
_____
_____
_____
_____
_____
_____
_____
_____
_____

Week Fifty (Tuesday): List some things you can do to make a difference in your employees' lives. It may be a raise. It may be a seminar you can send them to. List some ideas.

_____
_____
_____
_____
_____
_____
_____
_____
_____
_____
_____
_____
_____
_____
_____
_____
_____
_____
_____
_____
_____

Week Fifty (Wednesday): There are a small percentage of energy-draining patients in your practice who you need to let go. List them (by initials) and start thinking about a way to let them go. Hint: we talked about this before, but you must do this!

_____

_____

_____

_____

_____

_____

_____

_____

_____

_____

_____

_____

_____

_____

_____

_____

_____

Week Fifty (Thursday): Oftentimes we start to think too much of ourselves. What experiences have humbled you? How does that relate to your job as a DPC doc?

_____

_____

_____

_____

_____

_____

_____

_____

_____

_____

_____

_____

_____

_____

_____

_____

Week Fifty (Friday): Who are you here to be in this world? Maybe it is a doctor. Maybe it is more. Dream a little here.

_____

_____

_____

_____

_____

Week Fifty (Saturday): How did the week go? Pick out things that went well. Did you help people? What did you accomplish? What could you have done even better? How about those three small wins you wrote down on Sunday? Did you accomplish them? Or just review what you wrote each day and put some of your thoughts down here.

_____

_____

_____

_____

_____

WEEK FIFTY-ONE

Week Fifty-One (Sunday): It's time to plan your week again. Here are some things to think about, but feel free to only answer one or even something else entirely:

- What things can you do this week to become the doctor you've always wanted to be?
- What things can you do this week to work on your physical and mental self (working out, meditate, nature walks, sleep, reading, etc.)?
- What things can you do this week to improve your business (marketing, advertising, fixing the office, etc.)?
- Lastly, what three small wins do you want to accomplish this week?

Week Fifty-One (Monday): Take time to shut down all technology and stimuli. Sit with this notebook, or another one, and freestyle any ideas about your practice, your future, or your dreams. Let it rip. Your goal is to find ONE great idea.

_____

_____

_____

_____

_____

_____

_____

_____

_____

_____

_____

_____

_____

_____

_____

_____

_____

_____

_____

_____

Week Fifty-One (Tuesday): What is it about being a doctor that gives you the most joy? List some things.

_____

_____

_____

_____

_____

_____

_____

_____

_____

_____

_____

_____

_____

_____

_____

_____

_____

_____

_____

_____

_____

_____

Week Fifty-One (Wednesday): Have you done enough to network lately? What about with high-end business people? Mastermind groups? Can you start one on your own?

_____
_____
_____
_____
_____
_____
_____
_____
_____
_____
_____
_____
_____
_____
_____
_____
_____
_____
_____

Week Fifty-One (Thursday): How would your child or spouse describe you as a doctor? Pretend you are one of them and write down some adjectives. You can ask them for their thoughts after you are done. Compare.

_____
_____
_____
_____
_____
_____
_____
_____
_____
_____
_____
_____
_____
_____
_____
_____
_____
_____
_____

Week Fifty-One (Friday): Are you still celebrating your journey into DPC enough or maybe you haven't all done this at all yet? Sometimes we need to smell the roses, take a breath and appreciate our successes. List some things you can do to celebrate THIS week!

Week Fifty-One (Saturday): How did the week go? Pick out things that went well. Did you help people? What did you accomplish? What could you have done even better? How about those three small wins you wrote down on Sunday? Did you accomplish them? Or just review what you wrote each day and put some of your thoughts down here.

WEEK FIFTY-TWO

Week Fifty-Two (Sunday): It's time to plan your week again. Here are some things to think about, but feel free to only answer one or even something else entirely:

- What things can you do this week to become the doctor you've always wanted to be?
- What things can you do this week to work on your physical and mental self (working out, meditate, nature walks, sleep, reading, etc.)?
- What things can you do this week to improve your business (marketing, advertising, fixing the office, etc.)?
- Lastly, what three small wins do you want to accomplish this week?

Week Fifty-Two (Monday): What are some exciting plans you are working on? Don't have any? There is more to life than DPC. List some ideas here.

_____
_____
_____
_____
_____
_____
_____
_____
_____
_____
_____
_____
_____
_____
_____
_____
_____

Week Fifty-Two (Tuesday): What are the real sources of happiness in your job? How about in your life? Is it helping people? Is it about making money (there is nothing wrong with that)? List some sources.

_____
_____
_____
_____
_____
_____
_____
_____
_____
_____
_____
_____
_____
_____
_____
_____
_____
_____
_____

Week Fifty-Two (Wednesday): What things can you say "no" to in order to protect your time? Think deeply about this and list.

_____
_____
_____
_____
_____
_____
_____
_____
_____
_____
_____
_____
_____
_____
_____
_____
_____
_____

Week Fifty-Two (Thursday): What have you given away or volunteered for lately? Write down some examples of things you can give away or volunteer for.

_____
_____
_____
_____
_____
_____
_____
_____
_____
_____
_____
_____
_____
_____
_____
_____
_____
_____
_____
_____
_____

Week Fifty-Two (Friday): Knowing what you know now, would you change your pricing, keep the same staff, keep the same patients or do anything differently in your DPC practice?

_____

_____

_____

_____

_____

_____

_____

_____

_____

_____

_____

_____

_____

_____

_____

_____

_____

_____

Week Fifty-Two (Saturday): How did the week go? Pick out things that went well.   Did you help people? What did you accomplish? What could you have done even better? How about those three small wins you wrote down on Sunday? Did you accomplish them?   Or just review what you wrote each day and put some of your thoughts down here.

_____

_____

_____

_____

_____

_____

_____

_____

_____

_____

_____

_____

_____

_____

_____

_____

_____

To Ponder

Congratulations. If you have a chance, go back and look at what you have done over this past year. It's ok if you missed days. Just continue on and use these open spots daily until they are filled. Most importantly, there is a bunch of great information that YOU came up with. These are ideas you can teach others. These are ways you can use to motivate yourself. These are things to improve your practice. Great job!

Please don't ever throw this out. Keep it to reflect on now and later. In fact, I would recommend you spend time picking out some of your best ideas that you haven't completed and write them down in another notebook.

Lastly, I want you to know that what you are doing as a DPC doctor is important. You should be proud. You help others. You make a difference in peoples' lives. You may not get told that often enough. I want to tell you. I also want to make sure you take care of yourself while you are at it.

I wish you great success in your practice and in your life.

ABOUT THE AUTHOR

Douglas Farrago MD received his Bachelor of Science from the University of Virginia in 1987, his Masters of Education degree in the area of Exercise Science from the University of Houston in 1990, and his Medical Degree from the University of Texas at Houston in 1994. His residency training occurred way up north at the Eastern Maine Medical Center in Bangor, Maine. In his final year, his peers elected him chief resident. Dr. Farrago has practiced family medicine for twenty years, first in Auburn, Maine and now in Forest, Virginia. He founded Forest Direct Primary Care in 2014, which quickly filled in 18 months. Dr. Farrago invented the Knee Saver, a padding that relieves knee stress in baseball catchers, while he was in medical school. The original Knee Saver is currently in the Baseball Hall of Fame. He is also the inventor of the CryoHelmet worn by people for migraines, heat recovery and head injuries. Dr. Farrago created the *Placebo Journal* in 2001 and ran it until 2011. He is also the author of *The Official Guide to Starting Your Own Direct Primary Care Practice* (2016), *Diary of a Drug Rep* (2017) and *The Placebo Chronicles* (2005). Dr. Farrago still blogs every day on his website Authenticmedicine.com and lectures worldwide about the present crisis in our healthcare system and the affect it has on the doctor-patient relationship. He is a leading expert in the Direct Primary Care model and lectures medical students, residents and doctors on its benefits as well as how to start their own DPC practices.

Made in the USA
Lexington, KY
03 August 2018